MOVEMENTS OF MAGIC:
The Spirit of T'ai-Chi-Ch'uan

Bob Klein

NEWCASTLE PUBLISHING CO., INC.
North Hollywood, California
1984

Edited by Douglas Menville.

For information regarding T'ai-chi-Ch'uan classes, write to: Bob
Klein, P.O. Box 906, Miller Place, NY 11764.

A NEWCASTLE BOOK

First Printing April 1984

    2   3   4   5   6   7   8   9   10

Printed in the United States of America

To Mother Earth and all
those who work to protect her.

With grateful acknowledgement
to my T'ai-chi-Ch'uan teachers,
Master Herb Ray and Grandmaster
William C. C. Chen.

CONTENTS

PREFACE

The power and gracefulness of the creatures of nature exist potentially within each of us. We too are creatures of nature, and the feats of athletes, artists and scientists remind us of the power of our species.

Ancient cultures developed techniques to bring their people to the heights of their individual awareness, power and creativity. Sources of power our science does not yet admit exist were tapped in those times, enhancing the health and strength of the population. This is not merely legend, for some of those techiques and teachings survive today.

T'ai-chi-Ch'uan, the ancient Chinese teaching of living in harmony with nature, has gained a great deal of notice and popularity in recent years. Its versatility as a system of meditation, physical coordination, health, self-defense and consciousness raising has gained it many admirers.

T'ai-chi-Ch'uan is not a belief system or dogma, but a series of techniques designed to tap into and channel the powers of nature, both within and around us. Our modern technological age emphasizes the thinking mind, while other parts of our being, containing vast reserves of inner wisdom and power, are neglected.

T'ai-chi-Ch'uan reconnects the mind to the body, the consciousness to the subconscious and the individual to his environment. It ends the battles within you, eliminating tension and anxiety.

There is a natural creature within you which is the key to your well-being. It is this natural creature which has enabled our species to survive for our three-million-or-so-year history. It is the same force behind the survival and growth of all species for the past few billion years.

This force is called "Tai-chi" (or Tao).* It is very powerful and, in a sense, intelligent. We can determine certain laws in biological evolution and natural forces

---

*Taoism describes an individual Tao, which we know as the forces of nature, and the Great Tao, an indescribable emptiness latent with the potential of all existence. The Great Tao is unknowable and unnameable.

in general. These same laws hold from one day to the next and apparently from location to location.

If we could understand these forces and live in harmony with them, our lives would be much easier and more fulfilling. Science is attempting to do this. Yet science is not the first such attempt. The ancient cultures alluded to above have spent many thousands of years in the same quest, and we can profit greatly from a study of their findings. As science has benefited our material well-being, T'ai-chi-Ch'uan can benefit our health, emotional, psychological and spiritual—our inner well-being.

What follows is a precise description of the way in which this inner system is taught, the understanding of human nature it reveals, its practical applications to daily life, all of the specific techniques, the relationship between teacher and student and practical exercises anyone can do with or without a teacher.

Bob Klein

Sound Beach, New York
June 1983

INTRODUCTION

Through the midnight jungle a huge tiger silently edges his way between bushes and trees, a coiled spring of power in each step of his massive paws. Overhead, a thick python, well over twenty feet long, carefully glides over tree branches, focusing all its attention on the smell and the heat of the tiger. Quantities of power unimaginable to us seem poised within the giant serpent, waiting for just the right moment.

We humans can sense a degree of attention, a level of power in this scene which seems unattainable to us. It is almost mystical and other-worldly. Too often we accept sickness, emotional confusion, tiredness and feelings of helplessness as part of our lot as humans. And yet, we are part of the same natural system which has given rise to the tiger and the python, the soaring eagles and other awe-inspiring creatures.

A discipline exists which can raise each of us to such great levels of awareness, power, health and well-being, our true birthright as natural creatures of the earth. The practice of T'ai-chi-Ch'uan reunites the individual with the source of life itself, this great creature upon which we all live—the Earth. Through a series of natural meditative movements and other practices, the full potential within us is allowed to blossom.

Sources of energy known only to the wild animal and the young child are tapped. The body's healing ability is magnified. The mind and emotions are calmed, and tension and trauma are dissolved.

Additionally, T'ai-chi-Ch'uan serves as a self-defense system, physically, emotionally and psychically. Students are taught to be fully conscious in their dreams, to eliminate the barrier between conscious and subconscious parts of the mind and to relate to other people in a more spontaneous, natural and wholistic manner.

Based on a Chinese teaching over 6,000 years old called "T'ai-chi" (or Taoism), this discipline literally means "the Grand Ultimate Way of Life as taught through movement," or "Grand Ultimate Fist."

Its legendary beginnings describe Chang San-feng, a practitioner of hard-style (tension-oriented) Kung-Fu, watching a fight between a snake and a crane. The snake's looseness and concentration easily enabled it to evade the strikes of the crane. Chang San-feng developed a soft (internal power) style of Kung-Fu based on the lesson of the crane and the snake. For the past 1,000 years, teachers have developed and expanded this basic principle into a practical method of teaching T'ai-chi (Taoism), one of the cultural pillars of China. This philosophy is based on living in harmony with nature. Thus, this fighting style, expanded into an entire teaching system, has been called "T'ai-chi-Ch'uan."

This internal form of Kung-Fu is widely known as the system which uses the maximum amount of "chi" as opposed to external energy (muscle power). Chi is experienced as a universal energy all around us which is tapped or channeled by us in Kung-Fu, healing or any other activity. The amount of available chi is said to be limited only by the degree to which our skill can direct it. T'ai-chi students are often overwhelmed by the amount of chi flowing through their bodies.

To some, it is surprising to hear that Kung-Fu is actually a form of meditation. The T'ai-chi fighter must be in a state of meditation while sparring (fighting). Since there are no blocks in T'ai-chi Kung-Fu as such, the student must weave in and out between the punches and kicks. The degree of concentration and the speed of reaction time require calm, relaxation and spontaneity in the midst of very rapid movement. One never interferes with the momentum of the partner in sparring, but uses his momentum and strength against him.

Yet most T'ai-chi practitioners do not get involved in Kung-Fu, the dreamwork or most of the other teachings, but content themselves with the slow, flowing, meditative movements called "the Form." These movements are based on animal behavior and bring students into a harmonious relationship with their natural and human environment.

While most T'ai-chi-Ch'uan books concentrate on the Form, *Movements of Magic* has been designed as a comprehensive treatment of the entire range of T'ai-chi-Ch'uan practices, some well known, others rarely discussed, let alone taught. In addition, it will compare these practices with others such as Zen, Western mysticism and magic and Western science.

I have been told by many T'ai-chi schools that the "secret teachings" should never be revealed. To me this is nonsense. First of all, the world is in too precarious a state for anyone possessing valid instruction to withold it from the public. Second, I have found that the cry of "secret teachings" can often be translated as, "We really don't know what we're doing, but we like to sound mysterious."

This author has revealed all he feels is valid and worthwhile in this book, including his entire teaching method, the reasons behind each practice, their application to everyday life and the evolution in consciousness the student is likely to experience. On the other hand, you will find no pictures of the Form in this book. Such pictures are designed to be used along with ongoing classes. You cannot learn T'ai-chi solely from pictures any more than you can get proper nutrients from eating pictures of food.

Since each teacher may use a slightly different series of movements, the author feels uncomfortable recommending a book to his students with another school's Form. *Movements of Magic* can be used by any student of T'ai-chi-Ch'uan as well as by those simply wishing to enrich their understanding of ways to live a more harmonious and healthful life.

With such teachings as this readily available nowadays, there is little reason for poor health and emotional suffering anymore. It is common for people who feel they are dying or are contemplating suicide to join a T'ai-chi-Ch'uan school and gain much greater health and well-being than the average person. Perhaps they feel that practicing T'ai-chi couldn't be worse than death, so they might as well try it.

The Eastern approach to health, which is a wholistic approach, is attracting more and more notice from Western doctors. It is based on an "energy pattern" theory of disease rather than on a germ theory. A disturbance to the flow of chi is said to be at the root of much disease. This disturbance may be caused by a tense lifestyle, poor eating habits, a disconnection from the earth, extreme emotional pressure, behavioral programming or many other causes. The imbalance of bacteria within the body is seen as a secondary effect.

Heart attack patients are now turning to T'ai-chi as a way of reducing tension. T'ai-chi massage is a unique form of healing. Not only does it release deep seated trauma, it also sets up a nonverbal communication between the masseur and the individual muscle being massaged. This massage is sensitive to the response of the muscle. In this way it is not technique-oriented, but considers the muscle an intelligent, responsive entity. The persons being massaged learn a nonverbal "language" with which they may communicate with their own bodies. Their bodies thus become more alive and healthy.

From the Form to Kung-Fu, from dreamwork to healing, T'ai-chi-Ch'uan is a complete system of living in harmony with this natural world of which we are part. In almost every documentary on China, you will see people, young and old, practicing the Form in parks. It is now a required course in all schools of the People's Republic of China. Since T'ai-chi-Ch'uan is not a religion, it adapts well to any culture. We all wish to be healthy, calm and self-confident.

Movements of Magic is an expedition into a nature-oriented perspective and lifestyle whose origins reach back into prehistoric antiquity. At the same time it serves as a window by which to view the inner workings of other cultural systems. Most of all, it is a journey within yourself—a journey which has been taken by people since there were people on the earth. Take this journey! Who knows what you will find?

CHAPTER 1
THE FORM (I)

We love to watch clouds drifting in the sky or a puff of smoke gently swirling in the still air. The gentle soaring of a seagull fills us with a calm feeling. If only we could feel so calm within ourselves all the time.

The Form, a slow, relaxing series of movements based on animal behavior, is designed to develop calm, peace and gentleness within us. While each T'ai-chi-Ch'uan school has a slightly different Form, the principles on which the Form is based must be adhered to. These principles are the foundation of the entire teaching and are the culmination of thousands of years of the study of nature.

Smoothness

If we return to that seagull soaring about on currents of wind, we will find that the bird rarely flaps its wings. It is so sensitive to its own momentum and to the momentum of the air currents around it that it can remain aloft a long time, using little of its own energy. In our everyday life, we rarely pay attention to our own momentum because we feel we have enough energy to spare. We think of ourselves as comparatively massive creatures whose brute strength can compensate for a lack of delicateness.

But look at a creature even more massive than ourselves—the elephant. Elephants are so gentle that several can pass close to you in a jungle without giving themselves away. The idea that we can afford to waste energy in our movements has led to a depletion of energy in other areas of our being: health and instinctual wisdom, for example. Energy is like money. If we waste it, we won't have enough left for essentials. The Form reveals to us the ways in which we waste energy. By plugging up the leaks, we can begin to store up large amounts of power.

To discover these leaks of energy, the Form is done as slowly and smoothly as clouds drifting in the sky. The muscles learn to tense and relax slowly and smoothly. So slow is the Form that it resembles a slow-motion film or the animal called the slow loris.

Any patterns of tension within the body will become obvious and stand out against this flowing motion. Tension will pull that part of the body out of the smooth motion. The teacher points out to the student each tension pattern, no matter how miniscule, until the student returns to a smooth movement, consciously dropping the tension.

The Form, then, becomes a physical metaphor for your entire emotional state. Your internal state is displayed in external movement, and on that level can be dealt with more concretely. It is easier to correct a hand movement than an emotional habit.

Yet that correction in movement affects the emotional tension and actually dissolves it. For example, it is very difficult to be afraid of something while you are maintaining a relaxed state in all your muscles. The physical level of being, the emotional, the psychological and the spiritual are all connected. A change on one level affects all the other levels.

Slow, flowing movements of the body create an internal environment conducive to meditation. Your mind relaxes as your muscles relax, and the emotions soon follow suit. And yet the senses are still crisp and clear. Meditation through movement does not produce sleepiness. There is an odd combination of refreshed alertness and complete calm and relaxation.

Imagine waking up in a mountain forest. The sun is just appearing between two far mountains. Dew has washed the forest and bird sounds fill the air between the tall trees. You yawn, look all about you, smell the breakfast fire someone has started, and can hardly wait to begin the new day. The forest calls you to come out and play with it. This is the type of feeling the Form nurtures within you.

As you develop the smoothness of motion, your body begins to feel more liquid than solid. Rather than stepping from here to there, you seem to ooze like an amoeba. Feelings of rigidity fade away and you experience yourself in a new way. No longer does tension trap and harass you. The calm which has grown within you since you took your first lesson has become unshakable. Since this is a calm which has been gained through movement, it is an active calm and does not lead to sloth. It leads to your jumping out of the sleeping bag, downing a hearty breakfast and playing with the forest. This calm has been obtained from a loss of tension and anxiety and therefore a gain in energy, health and joy.

Lessons of the Form

Many lessons are learned from the smoothness of the Form. While smooth, the movements are not mushy, but crisp and precise. Each movement is clearly finished before proceeding on to the next. Our attention is focused on the present moment.

Often in life, we are so caught up in concentrating on the past and future that we miss the present. And truly, the present is all that exists for us. We may think about the past or imagine the future but we can actually deal only with the present. In the present, we have power.

When the mind jerks back and forth between past memories and future projections, the motion of the Form becomes choppy. If you are continually concentrating on your next move, you will begin that move before completing the present one. Thus the teacher can tell your state of mind from the quality of the Form you practice.

To concentrate on the present is to trust in the future and in your own power. As a present-minded student, you trust that in the next second you will make the proper movement. You don't have to think about it first. You don't have to check up on yourself. The next second, your inner power will be there to do the right thing, just as it is there this second. This inner intelligence, which we call Body-Mind (BM), does not need the thinking mind to tell it how to do the Form.

As a beginning student, you will use your mind to learn the Form, but at a certain point, the Form must become instinctual. This inner being (BM) does not worry or have anxiety. It simply acts. And it acts to create harmony within you and between you and your environment. The Form serves as practice for you to learn to trust your BM.

Momentum is felt as slow-motion waves flowing through the body. As an arm moves to the right, a wave of momentum slowly spreads through it until, reaching the fingertips, the wave slowly bounces back through the center of the body and perhaps into the opposite leg, which steps out next. Thus, these waves of momentum splash in slow motion from one part of the body through the center and into another part. It is a very sensuous experience.

Not one but many such waves are moving at the same time and interacting with each other. The student is aware of each interaction and attempts to prevent any one wave from meeting head-on with another. Such an interaction would neutralize energy, and one of the principles of the Form, as discussed above, is to avoid wasting energy.

It is obvious that the degree of concentration needed to keep track of such subtle internal interactions is extreme; yet it is not unusually difficult to achieve. Within two years most students are old hands at this game.

Any tension or rigidity is a block to this flow of momentum and will quickly become obvious. Since such blockages often lead to illness, the Form is really a game of maintaining health by eliminating blockages.

When a sufficient degree of looseness has been achieved, the body seems to float through the movements. The Form feels effortless, as if the body were being propelled by some outside force—a gentle breeze, perhaps. So slight is the energy needed to do the Form now and so great was it at the beginning of your training that you wonder, "Why did it seem so difficult?" You realize that a majority of the energy used initially was actually wasted in tension and distracting thoughts. The Form is done as effortlessly as blood flowing through your blood vessels, as a feather floating through the air. And you now realize that so much of your life can be this way—effortless and gentle, yet active and effective.

It is the union and harmony of mind and BM which leads to this state. Mind has been greatly developed in our society. T'ai-chi-Ch'uan emphasizes the development of BM. This internal, natural part of us is the center of creativity and play. The Form is an art which the BM can really "sink its teeth into" and thereby exercise its abilities. Motion is the canvas of this art, and the eddies and currents of the waves of momentum are the paints. BM paints a moving internal picture with momentum. Each eddy and current has its own set of qualities, just as each brush-stroke has its own quality and adds a new color to the canvas.

Your thinking mind sits back and asks, "How is this all going on?" You are not yet aware that BM is capable of many things, most of which you have never heard of and much of which will be described in later chapters. The Form gives you a hint of the power, creativity and playfulness of this inner being. Of its wisdom, you will soon discover much.

Another important lesson of the Form consists of the in-between places—the transitions from one movement to the next in which momentum gives out in one direction and begins a new direction. Logically, there should be a point at which the body comes to a complete halt. Yet this point is so imperceptable that you could say it does not exist. As the momentum gives out in an arm moving toward its own body, for example, the arm gradually slows down at the very end. As it begins its new direction, it gradually speeds up. Yet this alteration is so subtle that the arm appears to be moving at a constant speed. Due to this gradual slowing down and speeding up, the arm appears to be made of taffy. The entire body appears to be elastic or rubbery. "Like pulling silk out of a silk-worm cocoon" is the phrase most often used to describe this quality of the Form.

Such technical minutiae regarding the Form are great fun as long as we can laugh at ourselves. Otherwise, we will become depressed by our lack of coordination as revealed under the microscope of this teaching. When you are no longer tense and rigid, all you have left is laughter.

Rooting

The earth is calling to you. It has something for you. This great creature upon which we live wishes to give you its energy to empower your life. In Western culture, this great gift is shunned. We call it gravity and think of it as a force which tries to pull us down toward the center of the earth. Children are taught to "stand up straight" in an exaggerated posture with chest out and back arched to escape the force of gravity. It is difficult to understand how our attitudes towards this one concept, gravity, have affected our well-being. The religious concepts of hell below and heaven above, and of the lowly earthly flesh attest to the negative connotation of the downward direction. "God" is imagined as being in the sky, away from profane earthly matter.

In the physical experience of gravity, you can begin to understand how mental concepts can affect your actual perception. The very first thing a T'ai-chi-Ch'uan teacher will tell you is to relax your knees, hips and chest and imagine yourself hanging from the ceiling by a string connected to the very top of your head. Rather than pushing away from the earth with your feet, imagine yourself hanging in such a way that your feet are just touching the ground. You are like a marionette. In this state, gravity is experienced not as a force pulling you down, but as an energy filling you up. There is no need to fight gravity, for it fills you with energy. Thus a very basic conflict, that of trying to escape the pull of gravity, is dissolved and turned inside out. Ending this conflict has vast emotional, psychological and health benefits.

Often, you stand with locked knees, taking the weight off your leg muscles. In T'ai-chi-Ch'uan, the knees are always bent, at least slightly, so that the weight is allowed to sink through the leg muscles and feet into the ground. This is quite a different feeling from the usual experience of gravity. Rather than a pulling down, your experience is one of a dynamic connectedness. Earth energy is shooting up through your legs and roots are growing down into the earth, drinking up every drop of energy they can find. The metaphor of "Mother" Earth becomes very real. The term "rooting" refers to this feeling of roots growing down from the bottoms of your feet into the earth. These roots are composed of the feeling of your weight sinking through your feet.

The Sense of Energy

It is interesting to note that in many spiritual systems, the human being and life itself are represented as a tree. The Hebrew Qabalistic Tree of Life and the tree of life in Norse mythology are but two examples. (These will be explained in further detail in a later chapter.) Trees provide an accurate metaphor for the inner feeling of a T'ai-chi practitioner. Even the leaves absorbing warmth from the sun are part of the metaphor. As the energy from the earth fills you from below, there is a corresponding energy from above filling you downward. "Air" energy, as I call it, travels through your body, into the roots and is grounded in the earth.

The quality of interaction between these two forces and the way in which your creativity plays with them within your body is the source of chi (internal energy). Chi, therefore, is not something separate and independent within yourself, but a localized interaction of universal energies. Your body is a prism or lens capable of focusing and directing this energy for various uses. It is the skill of using this energy which constitutes an advanced teaching of T'ai-chi-Ch'uan, "Chi-Gung"— the teaching of chi. Chi-Gung is the core of T'ai-chi-Ch'uan.

Since the chi of one person is not separate from the energy of the planet as a whole, the individual is affected by the quality of energies around him. Visiting different people will change the feelings within you. A particular room will feel different, depending on who is in that room. One spot in a park will feel better to picnic in than another. Your environment affects you constantly. You can take advantage of this fact: if you are sensitive to the energies around you, you can use this sensitivity as a new sense—the sense of energy.

We are all familiar with the look of our bodies. We know, for example, that our body has two arms, two legs, hips, a chest and a head. If something else comes upon the scene, a dog, for example, we call this new object "external." It is the "other" and not part of us. If we did not know what we were physically, we would not know what was "us" and what was "other." This distinction of "self" and "other" lies at the base of using the sense of sight.

To develop the energy sense, you must do the same thing: focus in on the feeling of chi. How variable is it within you? Are there some aspects which always seem to be present? You actually begin to form an energy body—that is, a consistent quality of energy you can use as a reference point. In doing so, you have set yourself up at the center of a sort of spider's web. This center is the consistent energy pattern. The world around you will be compared to this central pattern, and thus you can map out the surrounding energy territory. This map is the web.

Once you have mapped out what you feel to be a fairly stable picture of your energy environment, you will "watch" for sudden changes in this environment. You will call those changes "intrusions" or "the other."

Sight works similarly. When you are sitting in a park, you are aware of your own body, then of the grass, trees and picnic tables surrounding you. If a bird should happen to fly by, you experience it as a momentary "intrusion" into an otherwise stable environment.

The spider's web is a sensing mechanism with which to experience the energies surrounding you. The basis of this ability is rooting. Rooting really means connecting to the environment. This connection is not confined to a downward direction; you can root in many ways and many directions. But the principle of rooting is easiest to understand as a downward connection to the earth.

The Body as a Spring

In order to properly maintain your rooting, the instructor will repeatedly adjust your posture to allow your full weight to sink through the feet. Correct posture requires a fairly straight back with only a minor natural curve in the small of the back. Knees are bent and the chest is relaxed. This posture is likened to a rearing snake and is actually an "S"-shaped curve. From the feet, the calves of the legs curve outward, then the thighs curve back inward. From the crease in the hips, where the legs meet the belly, the front of the body curves slightly forward.

This shape allows the body to behave in a spring-like fashion. A spring is able to absorb and release force by compressing and expanding. When a shock hits a spring, it compresses. Rather than being damaged, the spring merely stores the force that hits it, to be released later.

One of the lessons of rooting is the ability to absorb and use force. Physically, the legs act as cushiony shock absorbers, providing a yielding base for the movement of the upper body. The physical momentum of the upper body is constantly being absorbed and then released by the lower body.

If an outside force should hit the body, as in a push or a punch, this force is also absorbed into the legs. Should the force be formidable, it can be released into the earth from the legs and thereby be grounded out.

This way of dealing with physical force trains the emotional part of you to act in a similar manner. Emotional pressure is not fought or repressed, nor does it damage you. Such pressure meets with a firm but yielding emotional makeup—an emotional spring. There is no conflict. Excess pressure is released harmlessly. The recipient of the pressure views its sender as a source of energy and plays with that energy according to the lessons learned in the Form.

Push Hands, discussed in the next chapter, is the ultimate art of playing with another person's energy. There is very little that can phase a Push Hands player. The T'ai-chi temperament has often been likened to a large ocean wave. It is gentle and soft and yet, who can stop it?

Another metaphor for the quality of a T'ai-chi person in his dealings with the world is that of a peach. Within, there is a firm part called the pit. This firmness we will call "yang." Surrounding the pit is the soft meat of the peach, "yin." (Yin and yang will be discussed further in the next chapter.) In your dealings with the world as a T'ai-chi person, you are soft and yielding—yin. You do not look for conflicts and troubles but adjust yourself to each situation. But you won't be pushed around, either, for within you is a firm and rooted yang pit. You are sure of yourself and understand just how far you will go. When that point is reached, the spring is released. But this does not imply anger or overreaction, for when a spring is released, it is still pliable, even though it cannot be resisted.

The spring-like quality of the Form gives the impression of "something about to happen." If you've ever watched a snake about to strike at a mouse, you will have an appreciation of this quality. The snake's total concentration is on that mouse. Its body is frozen into an "S" shape, ready to strike. You watch with anticipation. Your own body seems taut with expectation. When will that power be released? Any moment now. . . .

All of a sudden, quicker than you can perceive, that mouse is within the snake's coils. In less than a second, your anticipation has been released. It is this feeling of expectation that the spring-like quality of the Form creates. You know the power is there and that it can be used at any moment. Feelings of power remain with you throughout your daily life, and thus you are relaxed, secure that it will come to your aid whenever needed.

Breath

This power, developed through rooting, is intimately tied to breath. Throughout spiritual literature the world over, breath is highly regarded as a key to personal development and internal power. In India, it is called "prana" or "life breath." Among the Gnostics and Hebrews it is known as the "breath of God."

There are some things that will be mentioned in this book which may seem strange, unscientific, fanciful, even uncomfortable to some people. Breath is one of those things. If I were to speak of the energy received from breath as being due to the intake of oxygen, there would be no problem. But I speak of breath in a different manner. This manner is not idiosyncratic to T'ai-chi-Ch'uan. On the contrary, the views on breath you will read below could have been written by a teacher in any one of a dozen or more spiritual or health systems throughout the world.

In order to convince you of the validity of these strange ideas of breath, I will suggest several breathing exercises for you to do. If you can experience personally what I am describing here, you will get much more out of this book.

Before you can develop internal energy, you must learn to take your breath from the ground—to breathe from the earth. It feels as though the breath is absorbed up from the earth, through the feet and into the body. As the breath is expelled, it seems to drain out of the body, through the feet and down into the earth. Without experiencing the breath in this way, the teaching of internal energy, so central to T'ai-chi-Ch'uan, would be very difficult. It is hard to say what is happening scientifically. Is there really an energy which the breath absorbs from the earth? To my knowledge, no scientific studies have been done to answer that question. As a T'ai-chi teacher, I can only tell you that experiencing the breath in this way is essential to progress in the art. Not only is the physical body rooted in the earth, but the breath as well.

Still another part of yourself must be rooted, and that is your attention. As the breath is released, the attention sinks into the earth like the breath. At the next intake of breath, the attention rises through the feet and fills the body. Attention may be thought of as the sap of a tree whose roots reach into the earth. The breath is the nutrient which feeds the tree.

Take time out now to do an exercise which will familiarize you with this important aspect of T'ai-chi-Ch'uan:

1. Stand with knees, hips and chest bent as if you were hanging by a string from your head. Feel the weight of your body on the bottoms of your feet. Relax the bottoms of your feet so that they do not grip the floor but merge with it.

2. Experiment with relaxing each muscle of the body separately until you know which ones are truly needed to hold you up. Of those, what is the minimum amount of tension needed to hold you up?

3. Begin to breathe slowly. The normal breathing rate during the Form is two in-and-out breaths per minute. If this is uncomfortable for you, simply breathe as slowly as possible. Diaphramatic breathing is essential. This type of breathing uses the expansion and contraction of the belly rather than the chest. Expand your belly on the inbreath; contract it on the outbreath. Keep your upper chest and shoulders relaxed at all times.

    a. Imagine the breath as a white mist passing up through your feet and into your body on the inbreath and draining out your feet on the outbreath. Imagine valves on the bottoms of your feet which must be kept open (relaxed) to allow the free flow of breath.

    b. Do not hold the breath either at the bottom or the top. Maintain an even speed of breathing throughout, except at the end of each outbreath and inbreath. Just before these points, begin to slow down your breathing rate. On the outbreath, for example, gradually slow down just before you reach the end. When you begin to breathe in again, gradually speed up to the normal rate. At no point should you exceed the normal rate, which is very slow and smooth. There is a tendency, when breathing slowly, to inhale quickly right after the outbreath. Avoid this impulse.

4. The same rules apply to the attention. Concentrate on the breath as it enters and leaves your body, allowing the attention to rise and fall as smoothly as the breath. Allow the attention to sink into the earth as far as it wishes. Feel the attention as a sinking weight. On the inbreath, feel the attention as a helium balloon rising up through your body, through the top of your head and into the sky. Allow "valves" on the top of your head to open, so that the attention and the breath may rise into the sky.

5. Try walking barefoot on the earth using this breathing exercise. As you step lightly with the advancing foot, breathe out. As you lift the rear foot, breathe in. You will become more sensitive to the feel of the earth on the bottoms of your feet. This exercise will make you feel like a creature growing out of the earth, and this you truly are.

Other Realities

T'ai-chi-Ch'uan is a teaching of life. Intellectually, we may know we are alive, yet few of us *feel* truly alive. This ancient Chinese teaching enlivens every cell of your body and reconnects you to the earth. When you feel connected to the earth, you feel a part of the earth and connected to everything else on the earth.

Your own roots seem to intermingle with the roots of all people and all creatures inhabiting this great living being, the earth. And don't be fooled into thinking that this is a metaphor. We have been trained to perceive the world in one way, and to us it seems quite real. But there are other ways to perceive the world which are just as real. T'ai-chi-Ch'uan opens the door to these other perspectives—these other worlds. Above all, it is a way to let go of the internal programming which confines you to only one perspective.

Of course, these are only words. The actual experience is the important thing. A T'ai-chi-Ch'uan teacher can be your guide on this journey to new worlds. But for those whose limited time or interest preclude studying this Chinese art of personal growth, the exercises outlined here will be of great help.

There is a Zen saying, "Give your flesh back to your mother and your bones back to your father and then show me your original face." Your parents and schooling programmed you to perceive this world and respond to it in a certain way. This programming was essential for your survival as a helpless child.

But now you are no longer a helpless child and must stand on your own. These perceptual tools—the programming—must be released for a time so that others may be tried. To let go of this programming, your grasp on the reality you know, may be a frightening step, yet it is filled with joy and power.

As you continue to read this book, feel your own reactions to the ideas which are presented. Perhaps you will find a part of yourself crying out, "Yes! This is for me!" That part is your Body-Mind, and in a very real sense I am writing this book for your BM. I hope to unite my roots with those of your BM, to encourage it with recognition. I want it to know that there is someone out there in the world rooting for it.

Many of us are so enthralled by the glitter of the modern world that we have become disconnected from our biological roots—our connections to nature. BM is this connection. Recognize it stirring within you as you read. This stirring may feel extremely pleasurable. On the other hand, it may feel threatening. If you (your mind) have been repressing this internal Body-Mind, it may be harboring a grudge against you. Should this be the case, the exercises described here will serve to alleviate the anger of your BM against you.

You will discover that without the aid of BM, you cannot root. You must root through BM, as BM is your connection to the earth. Without the aid of this natural internal creature, your life will never be filled with personal power. When mind and BM rejoin in a spirit of friendship, there is harmony once again within you. You may be rich, you may have great worldly power, but as a living creature of the earth, you will be a failure without BM. BM is the original face— the root of your being.

Connectedness

The Form develops your connection to the earth. It begins by connecting all parts of the body in a coherent, unified flow of motion. Movements of the arms and legs emanate from the movement of the hips and body in waves of momentum.

The arms move as if they are long balloons, floating in the air. As the body moves, the arms drift along with it.

To effect a punch, the weight shifts forward and the body turns, sending out an arm. To take a step, the leg drifts out and the weight of the body gently drains into the leg. All parts of the body seem geared into each other through the gear mechanism located at the center of the body, two inches below the navel, called the "Tan-tien."

The Form seems to just happen by itself, drifting along automatically, powered by some outside force. It does not appear as if you are making yourself move; you feel as if the Form were taking place without your conscious intent. Your attention is not standing apart from your body, directing your actions, but is flowing along with the momentum. Your breath is flowing in and out exactly, according to the pace of your movements. Thus your body and all its parts, the attention, momentum and breath are all connected and flowing together as one unit. It is impossible for you to distinguish one part from the other within yourself; they all seem to be elements of one common force—chi.

Harmony of Mind and BM

It is BM which directs chi and thus directs the Form when it is connected. One day you may be in the middle of the Form and suddenly remember you have to do something else. Your mind will try to get you to stop the Form, but your BM will prevent the Form from ending. BM has refused to allow the mind to disrupt its activity. It has grown as powerful as the mind.

This internal being, guardian of health and spiritual well-being, is now in a position to challenge the supremacy of the logical, thinking mind. Being as jealous of power as it is, mind will not take this challenge mildly. It will do all within its power to regain its supremacy by disconnecting you internally and separating you from your natural environment. This is a valuable time for you because now you can learn all the mind's tricks (and mind will use every trick in the book!).

First it will try to convince you to stop practicing T'ai-chi. Then it will try to reconnect you to old patterns of behavior. You may start complaining that the Form is too boring or time-consuming; you may want to eat junk food or smoke cigarettes to dull your nervous system. Patterns of tension, long since dropped, may arise again. The mind will begin nonstop thinking to keep you mesmerized, or it will use its henchman—TV.

Watch your behavior. See how it changes once the thinking mind is challenged by the natural self. You will learn how you have been disconnected from your feelings, from those around you and from natural sources of energy. But don't worry over the outcome of this contest, for the Form has been designed to create a harmonious partnership between mind and BM. As long as you continue to practice, a positive outcome is assured.

With mind and BM equal in power, the entire nature of your being changes. Mind wants to remain in power for the same reason politicians want power—to amass great wealth. The wealth of the body is attention energy. It is this energy which is used to draw on the flow of energies in the environment. If mind captures attention energy, both body and mind are made to suffer because then it is more difficult to absorb energy from the environment. A power-seeking mind is not a clear and stable mind, nor does it reside in a healthy body. It can disconnect your entire being from your source of true power—the earth.

When power is shared, all parts of yourself are receiving equal energy. The attention is centered in the Tan-tien, the physical center of the body, and not in the thoughts or even the senses.

Your five senses can also grab a disproportionate share of this valuable energy. In Zen they have been called the "five thieves." Any area of the body that grabs and holds onto a disproportionate share of the attention weakens the whole organism. The ability of internal energy to move freely from one area to another, depending on need, is a basic essential to health. The term "connected" really refers to a condition in which all areas of your being are open to each other and to the environment. It is chi which connects all the parts.

While the principles of connectedness are taught by having all the physical parts of the body move in synchronization during the Form, the implications of this lesson are vast. Connectedness and openness are essential in health, human relationships, spiritual development and the ability to be relaxed and energetic.

While the Form is connected, it is not stiff. There is a little play in the connections between arms, hips, legs and body, as well as between the fingers, palms, forearms, upper arms and the parts of the legs. Even the chest moves in a fluid manner and must be flexible within itself. The Form is a strange combination of connectedness and fluidity, of being rooted into the ground and yet floating.

An exercise you can do to get this feeling is to move in slow, animal-like movements in a pool or other body of still water. Watching students going through the Form, you get the impression that they are moving through a viscous liquid. And in a sense this is true, for students must be so sensitive that even air, light as it is, feels like a viscous liquid to them. And they are also moving through another medium—energy. Their sensitivity to energy gives them a feeling similar to moving through water filled with eddies and currents.

That natural being within you will gain power just from watching someone do the Form. It seems to say, "Yes, there's something about that. . . ." The mind, however, will say, "That's silly," and will laugh at the Form. There is a T'ai-chi saying, "When a fool sees the Tao, he laughs, otherwise it would not be the Tao." But it is nervous laughter, for mind suspects what the Form is for. Ridicule of the Form is one of its tricks. The Form is Toto the dog in *The Wizard of Oz*, pulling aside the curtain that hides the thinking, logical mind.

"Don't pay attention to that man," mind says, "Fear Oz; be attracted to the glitter. Never find out that the power of the universe is within you."

Once you are connected to that power and thus connected to the earth, fear is an illusion. It is an ordinary man behind a curtain.

Relaxation—Letting Go

Many people are drawn to T'ai-chi-Ch'uan because it enables them to let go of their tension permanently. Without tension, anxiety and worry, life is a lot more enjoyable. To the martial artist of an internal power style of self-defense, it is especially important to let go of tension, for it slows down the body, reduces the power of punches and kicks and drains the fighter's stamina.

Once your tension is released, internal energy can flow unimpeded throughout your body. But to release this tension, you must go through the nervous system, for it is a nerve, constantly sending its signal to a muscle, which causes that muscle to tense. You are making yourself tense; to eliminate that tension, all you have to do is stop causing your muscles to tense. Tension, therefore, is not released by doing something extra, but by letting go of something you are already doing.

Letting go is a basic, if not *the* basic principle of T'ai-chi-Ch'uan. It is said that a student's progress is determined by how much he is willing to let go of—tension, emotional programming, fear, thinking, defensiveness, etc. The natural being is already powerful and wise. You must let go of your interference with the body's power and wisdom.

An important obstacle to overcome is the feeling that you are holding yourself together. The physical experience of relaxing is often misinterpreted by the mind as falling, letting go of your defenses, being vulnerable and turning into mush.

Notice what happens when someone challenges you. Muscles all over the body tense as if to prepare for a fight, whether the challenge is physical or intellectual. A proper use of the logical mind would tell you that when you are tense, your muscles are battling each other. Opposing sets of muscles are pulling against each other. So instead of preparing to do battle with an opponent, you are really battling yourself.

Watch yourself when you feel long-term anger toward another person. Again, muscles tense, your stomach turns and you feel very bad inside. Here too you are not doing anything against the object of your anger; you are only harming yourself. The key to well-being is to end these internal hostilities. They will not improve your life. They will only make it more and more difficult for you to meet your real needs.

A story was told to me about a sunken ship which many salvage operations tried to raise. It was buried beneath tons of mud. After a fortune was spent trying to recover the ship, someone thought of a simple idea. When the tide was out, he brought a barge directly over the sunken ship. Divers attached ropes and chains from the barge to the ship. Then, when the tide came in, the barge rose with the water, lifting the ship out of the mud.

Relaxation is much like the barge. Our angers and frustrations are the mud which keeps us submerged all our lives. We resist being raised out of these self-righteous negative feelings. Yet, when we learn to relax down to the last nerve and muscle cell, these feelings simply slough off and we are once again light and free.

Letting Go of Mind

The internal battles of the mind must not be allowed to take over your body. To test the degree to which your mind has conquered your body, do the arm-lifting exercise. One person simply lifts your arm and moves it around at the shoulder. You must keep that arm completely loose and relaxed. The lifter feels for even the slightest hint of tension on your part. This tension will be felt as the arm suddenly becomes lighter or locks into position. If the arm is tense, you will know that you are no longer in control of your own body. The mind has taken control, and the battles of the mind have spilled out into the body.

How has this happened? You are taught to fear your natural feelings, to feel inadequate and incompetent. You are led to believe that only the mind, with its logic and storehouse of facts, can save you. The mind proclaims that it is holding you together, protecting you from the world. And so, just as we yield power to our leaders, you give power to your mind, forsaking your internal feelings.

The thinking mind functions in a dualistic manner, with one idea battling another, one viewpoint competing with another. As the mind gains control over the body, it causes the body to function similarly. It creates the body in its own image. But bodies are not designed to function that way. The elegance of the movements of wildlife attest to this.

The Form returns your body to its natural functioning and your mind to its proper place. As your tension is released, your mind is rightfully afraid of losing its power. This is the fear of falling associated with learning to relax. Since your mind has convinced you that it must fight these battles for your protection, relaxation also causes you to feel vulnerable. Yet that vulnerability is a key to power. It's more sensitivity and openness than vulnerability. You're more aware of what is going on around you and can respond more effectively.

The battles of the mind are the issues you try to resolve as you progress through life. Let's examine one of these issues to understand how they keep you from relaxing. By understanding how they control your behavior, you will discover what you have to let go of in order to be free.

One common issue is: Am I better than other people? Do I have better looks and personality? Do people like me more than others? Am I smarter, stronger, more humble, healthier, more spiritual, do I smell better, dress better, am I less materialistic, etc., etc.? In this case, your behavior is directed by a particular value system as you believe others perceive it. Your goal is to look good in the eyes of others; therefore, you have yielded your own power to them. No longer is behavior emanating from BM, from the natural sense of harmony within you.

Watch a robin splashing in a little puddle of water on a newly sprinkled lawn. Does it splash because it thinks this makes it a good bird? Probably not. Yet who, watching the pure delight in its movements, can deny that it is enjoying its splashing? It is the satisfaction of the cool water which brings joy to that robin.

In our modern world, there is so much more than a small puddle of water to bring us joy, yet we often lack the simplicity to appreciate it. The great secret is that nobody is really looking at you. They are concerned with themselves. The same insecurity which is driving you to yield your power to them is causing them to yield their power to you. You should feel honored that they are concerned about your opinion of them.

Life's great task is to create. We can create ourselves as an artist creates a painting or a song. The feeling of that song wells up within him and bursts forth as a flower blossoms. Nature has created her art and we are part of it. We need not search for the answers to our lives in this philosophical system or that. We need not constantly watch ourselves to make sure we are behaving exactly according to the proper social rules.

Trusting the Monster

Don't you trust yourself? Don't you trust that you are a good human being who, if allowed to do whatever you wished, would do positive and loving things? What lies have you fallen for? Have they frightened you into believing there is a monster within you? It's not a monster. It's Body-Mind, your own true self. BM is the artist within you, the true creator and apprentice of Nature herself.

And yet, so much of our lives is spent trying to measure up to standards. If we give up this endeavor, wouldn't there be a great emptiness? Wouldn't we stop striving and become dull? Not at all. How exciting is it for you to worry, to be anxious that you don't measure up? Isn't that what is keeping you from feeling vital and looking forward to each day?

When you let go of tension by practicing the Form, issues such as these drop away, but not because you try to drop them. You no longer force yourself to measure up to yet another standard by coercing yourself into *not* thinking certain thoughts. The teacher merely corrects a hand movement here and a tension in the shoulders there. Before you know it, the old patterns of behavior have become boring and you no longer have any interest in them. They have lost their appeal.

Yet the sight of a sunset, the taste of an orange, the love of a friend, the joy of a discovery all gain in appeal. BM is in the world, seeking its pleasures and fulfillment. Emotional turmoil, aggravation and anxiety are not pleasurable to it, so it won't engage in those activities. No, BM is not a monster. It is your true self. It is the earth within you.

Letting the World In

Not only does the Form relax the muscles and nerves, but the senses as well. When students are urged to "let go with your eyes," of course they reply, "I'm not grabbing anything with my eyes." But they are. The perspective we have grown up with during modern times is one of separation. We feel like isolated objects within a world of objects. This is not a fact but a perspective. Children, before they are molded into this perspective, experience the world as being part of themselves. At a very young age they have not yet learned to divide their world into "self" and "other." There is thus a natural flow of energy between them and the world.

The reason babies and children cry so much is not because that's just the way it is. In my opinion it's because they are being cut off from energy by being taught our perspective. If someone were to cut off your oxygen supply, you would complain too. The universal energy feels as vital to a child as oxygen does to you. It is the oxygen of BM.

As adults, we long for that energy. We seek it in love, food, entertainment and through the senses. We try to grab it from the sensory scene around us without realizing we are doing so or understanding what we seek. This attempt at grabbing energy from the environment leads to a deepening of the feeling of separation.

While doing the Form, students are taught to "soften" their eyes—to scan the scenery around them passively and allow the sights to flow into their eyes. The eyes must not show intent. They must not dart here and there, holding onto particular objects, seizing them as raw materials for the mind to categorize. Concentrating on particular objects to learn to focus attention will be learned later. First, your eyes must learn passivity so that the chi may flow in and out of them.

But the senses are not the only part of you that tries to grab. Your hands too must learn to relax so that energy can flow in and out of them. Energy must be allowed to flow out through the skin as well, forming a spherical field around your body. Luckily for the T'ai-chi student, this energy is felt vividly and not just intellectually assumed to be there. Over and over again students ask, "How is this possible? How can we feel such things?" It is sad that they even have to ask.

Letting Go of Self

One of the most damaging "areas" for a person to be tense in is personal identity. We are afraid to change, to become different from what we are now. Our identity is perceived as a protection and we defend it at all costs. Yet without change, how can we grow? We *will* grow, no matter how hard we try not to. Just remember back five or ten years ago. Are you the same person now you were then? Your name may be the same, you may live in the same house and have the same memories, yet your behavior may have changed. Certainly, the atoms which compose your body have changed. Your opinions, friends and tastes may have changed. Different thoughts pass through your mind each second. Your senses record different scenes each moment.

Change is the basis of life. The ability to deal with change, to influence its speed and direction, is the power we have as humans. Children need to identify themselves, to carve out their niche, to be recognized for their qualities. Imitation of parents and peers is essential in learning the rules of society's games, so that the child may survive. In this imitation process, the child is acquiring patterns of behavior and building his personality. He is collecting the raw material for behavior as a wood carver collects pieces of wood for future carvings. Yet few of us become carvers ourselves; we are just collectors of other peoples' behavior. We identify with this pile of behavior. If you can remember back to childhood, this self-identification took tremendous effort and attention. While valuable as a stimulus to learning, children's self-identification process places their power in the hands of those around them. Identity, or ego, the feeling of self, thus becomes a handle by which others may control you if it is anchored in the past and used for security.

T'ai-chi turns the self-identification process into an artistic medium. You learn to carve the wood. By identifying with BM, the artist of life, and thereby with creativity itself, your identity becomes a canvas upon which BM may paint beautiful pictures. Alterations in the structure of self-identity are not caused by your perceptions of other peoples' opinions of you, but by your own creativity. The process of self-identity is fluid, and thus growth can take place.

Notice the difference in approach between T'ai-chi and traditional Western psychology. In the West, personal problems are seen as flaws in the personality structure. Growth is seen as a change from one structure to another. Fluidity of the personality structure is the essence of the T'ai-chi version of psychology. Just as water in a stream is able to flow around the rocks and fallen branches in its path, the personality, the very energy pattern of a person, must be flexible enough to flow over life's rocks.

Skill in flexibility will allow you to adapt many patterns of interaction to your environment. Watch yourself as you interact with different people. You will act differently toward your child than toward a salesperson and differently still toward your landlord. Varying situations call for varying responses. Flexibility of behavior makes you effective in everyday living.

But if your behavior is varying, you may ask what is the "real you"? The real you is that natural creature, the center of creativity, your connection to the earth creature. What is this creature and what does it feel like? When you have a sudden insight, when you laugh, when you love, when the summer sunshine reaches within you and reminds you what joy feels like, then you are feeling BM. When a new song comes to you from out of the blue, it comes from BM. Tension and anxiety are a barrier to this being. Through physical relaxation, the Form relaxes the other levels of your life as well and allows BM to step out into the world.

Letting Go of False Protection

The thinking mind has done a good job. It has protected BM from the dangers of the world, at least in its own eyes. You must thank mind for its help. It is, after all, part of you. But now you are grown up, and BM must make it on its own.

You stand at the gate of the walled city in which you live. The huge iron gate of mind is raised and BM begins its journey into the world. Do not worry, for BM is immortal, it is Tao. It does not need a wall around it for protection, only a self-awareness. BM has remembered the substance of which it is made—pure creativity—and knows the only thing which can harm it are the walls which have kept it prisoner all these years.

The inner being passes through the gate and looks back. "Come," it calls to mind, "for you are part of me. You are my creation. You are a tool I once used before I forgot myself and let you use me. Let us sojourn together as equals—you, the mighty warrior, with your facts, knowledge and calculations, and I, with my creativity, love and gentleness. We will explore this world together."

Thinking mind relaxes, the walls soften and you are a whole being once again.

This story is the theme of many legends throughout history. Some of these legends and their T'ai-chi interpretations will be discussed in a future chapter.

The way in which people deal with tension is vividly revealed on roller-coaster rides. As the ride goes over the top and plummets, the riders divide into two categories: some grab the handlebar which holds them in their seats, tense up and scream (or close their eyes). Waves of adrenalin splash through their bodies as fear paralyzes every part of them. Try to release their grip from the handlebar and you will feel the extent of their tension.

Then there are those who try to get into the first car, lean over the edge of their seats and all during the ride, wave their hands in the air and laugh. They seem to say, "Scare me! I love it!"

After riding a dozen or so times in a row, you find that your attention has centered in the Tan-tien, that area two inches below the navel. As you plummet over the edge, your body quickly realizes that your mind is of no help in this situation and that you'd better rely on BM, which is centered in the Tan-tien.

Not only do you feel rooted, but you couldn't stop feeling rooted if you wanted to. Your body knows that its power lies in its connection to the earth. Your energy sinks to the center of that connection and won't come out until it's sure the coast is clear. Yet, your body is not tense. When shocked, it prepares for flight or fight. This is a natural response. Neither fighting nor fleeing can be accomplished with a tense body.

Letting Go of Addiction to Mind

The mind tenses up in fearful situations because it realizes that it's really helpless. Only BM, with its spontaneity, sensitivity, speedy reactions, power and connection to the power of the earth, can protect you in severe circumstances. If mind has been repressing BM, your power has been locked up, and then mind is paralyzed with fear. It is afraid to release BM, for BM may not be so easy to lock up again, yet it is also afraid of the situation facing it.

Mind is in a difficult position. To expect that you can solve the situation through using the mind is unreasonable. (For example, that roller-coaster car is going over the top no matter what ideas the mind can come up with. Another example is death; you can't think your way out of it.) The attempt to resolve internal conflict through the use of the mind, as is done in conventional therapy, usually drags out for many years. Through relaxation of body and mind, and allowing BM to gradually gain strength, your rate of personal growth is accelerated.

Letting go of the dictatorship of mind is called "not doing" or "no mind" in both T'ai-chi and Zen. A fine tool, developed over thousands of years, has been allowed to take over your entire being. If you were truly a craftsperson of the mind, you would know how to use this tool. You use a hammer to drive nails into wood. If you want to turn a screw, you must put the hammer down and use a screwdriver. But you not only try to use a hammer to turn a screw, you carry that hammer around with you wherever you go.

Meditation teaches you to set the tool of mind aside once in a while. Moving meditation shows you that without mind, you can still function well. While you are active, the activity seems effortless because you aren't thinking your way through it. It just seems to happen by itself. This is "not doing." It is a feeling of joyful emptiness, the emptiness of the moon refleceted on a still lake. No disturbance is felt by the lake, yet it reflects the moon with crystal clarity. Within you, the everyday circumstances of life no longer trigger tensions and preprogrammed behavior patterns. Each moment is experienced with crystal clarity and calmness. Your mind can no longer convince you to get upset.

It's hard to know how much control the mind has gained over you, so we practice exercises designed to release the grip of mind. Try one: Next time a thought pops up in your mind, refrain from thinking the thought out in words. You'll find that a thought is instantaneous; it doesn't need to be translated into words. With practice, you'll catch yourself in time, as soon as the thought pops up, and will experience the thought not as language, but as an entire pattern of energy or feeling.

If you were to try to express how delicious your dinner was to a person not conversant with English, you might put your fingers to your lips and kiss them, then throw them into the air. This action is universally understood. When word-thoughts have been dropped, there is still an internal system of direction and understanding. This system is the movement and vibration of your energy pattern, the language of action. Thoughts as we know them, that is, words, are either a translation of this pattern or a repetition or rearrangement of someone else's words. Too often, it is this second form of thought which is prevalent. This type of thinking is not a description of what your awareness tells you, but a parroting of word-patterns heard before.

To accomplish true thinking, you must first be aware. Then the words which emanate from your mouth are descriptions of what you have actually experienced and not a regurgitation of something you previously swallowed. BM is the part of us which experiences and is aware. If mind is suppressing BM at the same time it is issuing forth its ideas, then those ideas are not grounded in awareness.

Mind is mesmerized by hearing itself talk and by the clever way it manipulates words. But those words can never be a substitute for the fulfillment of direct experience—a fulfillment attainable only by BM. When mind translates for you the tales of the journeys of BM, it is fulfilling its true purpose. Within mind resides all the knowledge of who you are and of what you are and are not capable of doing. When you let go of mind, you let go of your limitations, of the walls of the city within which you think you must remain.

A story is told of Millipede, with his innumerable legs. Grasshopper walked up to him and asked, "With all those legs, how can you keep them all coordinated?" Millipede thought about it for a moment . . . and then he was paralyzed. He could no longer walk.

"No self" or "not being" is a dropping of the concepts of who you are and what you can do. Nothing has really been destroyed; instead, limiting concepts are no longer allowed to take over and entrap you.

The Lessons of Letting Go

In Kung-Fu, beginning students are hurt every time they are punched in the face. Yet after several months of practice, punches of even greater force do not hurt. Most of the hurt is actually emotional and related to the fear of having their personal space invaded, of being faced with aggression. Emotional fear, triggered by the punch, is the real source of hurt. Pain, the physical experience of the punch, does not actually hurt much. As the students drop their emotional fear of the punch, the amount of hurt lessens.

Even your posture within the Form has an emotional content. A slouched posture may indicate a negative self-image or a feeling of being burdened. By correcting the posture, your entire emotional climate can be changed. Correct posture requires relaxation. T'ai-chi-Ch'uan posture also requires a relaxation of the ankles and the bottoms of the feet. As weight shifts from one leg to the other, the momentum feels as though it were flowing along several levels—the bottoms of the feet, the ankles, the knees, the hips and the chest. Each of these areas must remain relaxed. The body does not move up and down in the form,* but remains at a constant level. Forms done with the body bobbing up and down show that the movements have not been internalized.

When the posture is relaxed, the weight seems to fall through the feet even as it moves horizontally through the various levels of the body. At the same time, the body is also turning on its axis with many of the movements. Interactions among horizontal, vertical and circular flows of momentum produce the "splashes" of momentum discussed previously.

At each point in the Form, there is a characteristic pattern to these interactions, depending on the style in which the Form is done. We play with the interactions, trying different pattens of energy flow by altering the style of the Form. Playing with the pattern of momentum is really a metaphor for playing and experimenting with your energy pattern, behavior and identity.

In all the styles, relaxation is maintained. It is said that if a fly were to land on a student's hand, the hand should be sensitive enough to drop from the weight of the fly. As the hands move through the air, they must be so sensitive to it that they do not hit it broadside but slice throught it with their edges. Gentleness must be developed to such a degree that even the air is not interfered with.

From the Taoist text, the *Tao-te Ching*, we learn that

When Man is born, he is tender and weak.
At death, he is stiff and hard.
All things, the grass as well as trees, are tender and supple while alive.
When dead, they are withered and dried.

Therefore, the stiff and the hard are the companions of death.
The tender and weak are companions of life.
Therefore, if the army is strong, it will not win.
If a tree is stiff, it will break.
The strong and the great are inferior, while the tender and the weak are superior.**

---

*Except for special moves, such as "squatting down" and "needle at sea bottom."
**The Way of Lao Tzu, translated by Wing-Tsit Chan. The Library of Liberal Arts, Bobbs-Merril Co., Indianapolis & N.Y.

CHAPTER 2
THE FORM (II)

We think back with fondness to the innocence of youth. But for most of us there is a time beyond which we cannot remember events, let alone the feelings of the formative years, those years during which our programming was installed. One of the uses of the Form is to enable you to remember back to your earliest days. The major stumbling block is that now your memory is controlled by mind, while during your earliest years, before the mind's growth, BM had supremacy.

Memory was recorded by mind. Consequently, the methods you use to recall memories will not work for the times when BM was in control. Remembering your infancey gives you a clear picture of how you were programmed and makes it much easier to drop programming that you feel is harmful to you.

Feeling Memory

To remember your infancy, you must use "feeling memory." As you practice the Form, you become more and more familiar with the patterns of momentum of each movement. Once these patterns have really become part of you, you can drop your mind, that is, you no longer need to direct your movements by thinking about them. You *feel* your way through the movements.

Learning to drive a car is similar. At first you must think about each move, but soon, driving becomes automatic. You may be driving for a while and then suddenly realize that you haven't been paying attention to your driving. Something within you has done it automatically.

Growing Up

It is strange to contemplate what your world was like before you developed your understanding of it. How much different was it then than now? Now you know what to look for in the environment. You know what is important for you to discover about your world and what it means. For some, the facial expressions of other people are important, for they give clues to what the other person is thinking. Farmers often gaze at the sky to judge the weather. Should they irrigate today or will it rain anyway? Workers within a corporate structure look for opportunities to advance themselves while watching out for stabs in the back from those who want their jobs.

What is it that a child, innocent of your knowledge, looks for in the environment? BM is in control and its function is homeostasis—the proper functioning of the body through the balance of chemicals, energy flow, temperature, etc. The behavior of a child emanates from this need for balance. Emotions stem from the interaction of the need for homeostasis and the interference of this process by the environment. Feelings of well-being are the result of a proper flow and balancing of energies.

But in each culture, the child must be taught a form of magic. Magic is a structure of knowledge allowing him to work his will within a particular system. In our society, that magic is all the knowledge and techniques we have at our disposal: math, reading, writing, science, art, medicine, etc. So the child goes through disciplines which oppose this homeostatic need. He will have to delay his immediate homeostatic needs in order to gain the knowledge and skills necessary for his future well-being. He may have to push himself beyond his endurance and concentrate intensely on his studies.

The degree of well-being of this child will depend to some extent on whether the magic of his culture is based on balance and nature or not. A system which requires him to interfere with the homeostatic mechanisms, including the flow of energy in and out of his body, will result in poor health and unhappiness. In this case, the inner awareness of the balances and imbalances of the body gets pushed to lower and lower levels of consciousness. The origins of ill feelings are hidden deeper and deeper. Feeling memory, which is based on the homeostatic mechanisms, is also hidden.

To recall such memory would require recalling the ways in which your well-being was interfered with and repressed. This would be difficult to face. It would mean admitting that the very society which is the source of your security is in actuality the source of your ill-being.

What can you do—become a hermit? Leave society? You can find others with the same awareness and create your own little society within the larger society. You can build a model of a society based on nature, or copy such a society from an existing model.

Learning to Be a Child

In your own life, you can become aware of the causes of your ill-being and rebuild your life around more natural principles. In order to become more aware of what you need biologically to develop your well-being, it's helpful to remember back to the days in which the natural forces within you were more in balance.

The Form focuses your attention on your feeling memory. It enables you to pay attention to those things the child was aware of—to look at the world through the eyes of a child while retaining the wisdom and knowledge you have gained as an adult. It can even make your body more flexible and energetic, as it was in your youth.

All the principles taught in the beginning of this discipline are those the child is already aware of. Watch a small child standing in a supermarket shopping cart lift a box of food from the cart and place it on the conveyer belt. He uses his whole body; his entire attention is focused on that object. Watch small children in a car on the road. They stare all around them, not wishing to miss any of the scenery. Watching the scenery is extremely pleasurable for them, because energy flows unimpeded into and out of their eyes. Then look at their parents. Are the parents' eyes as wide-open?

Returning Home

Often while doing the Form, you may be amazed at the feelings within you. Those feelings have a certain quality you have experienced before, here and there, but were never able to understand. They feel as if they were signposts written in some long-forgotten language, leading to a place you know you want to go, if only you could remember. . . .

At first, you must content yourself with merely experiencing those feelings and becoming familiar with them. It is as though you were visiting a foreign country with a different language and customs. Intricacies of rules of conduct, the meaning of gestures, sources of food and shelter, values of local money, etc., would take time to learn.

But in the case of feelings of internal energy flows, you are in a much better position. You have a guide who already knows his way around. This guide is BM. All you have to do is wander through the "town" and search for your guide. You let it be known that you are searching for BM through your practice of T'ai-chi-Ch'uan. Soon, BM will come looking for you. This is before you realize that BM *is* you.

At this point in your training, you will sense that there is something within you which seems to know its way around the world of energy. You'll try to understand what you are being shown, but you will face a dilemma. No matter how hard your mind tries to interpret the energy "scenery"—homeostatic activities—it will not be able to do so. The logical mind is not designed for that. It only knows what society has taught it. It knows how to interpret the world around it in only one way.

So you are faced with a decision. In order to become familiar with the energy world, you must release your attention from mind and jump down into BM. The fear of this jump is that it may be only one way. Will mind be lost forever? At some point, that jump has to be made, but for now the cliff seems too high. So you are allowed to take several small jumps (termed "satori" in Zen).

First, you must pay attention to the mechanics of the movements of the Form. This arm goes here, that foot goes there, thirty percent of your weight is on this foot, seventy percent on that foot, etc.

Next, you must concentrate on the smoothness of the Form, then the rooted-ness, connectedness, relaxation, internal energy, etc. Little by little, more attention is focused on the internal workings of your body. At the same time as the attention is brought within the body, the thinking process is taken out of the body. When your attention has been partially released from the thinking mind and you see that there are no harmful effects, you will gain courage to release the mind even more. Finally, all of the attention can be focused on the balancing system of the body and its connections to the environment.

At that moment, a strange thing happens. You take a look around you and notice that something is different. There is an element of the world around you which was not there before. The world seems suddenly to come alive. An intimacy between yourself and the environment, a feeling of being rooted into everything through your connection to the earth, suddenly manifests. A missing magical ingredient has suddenly appeared in everything; that ingredient is chi. It is the energy connecting you to all things. There is no longer any need for your eyes to grab the scenery around you, for you are already connected to it. You have found that secret place, that ancient paradise of legend, and it is the very world around you. You realize that time itself is a legend. Thinking back to all the things your T'ai-chi teacher told you and all you read in T'ai-chi books, now you understand.

You are now perceiving the world without the intermediary of mind. This is direct perception. It is poignant; it touches you deeply. Now when you watch animals staring for long periods of time into the environment, you realize that it's not because they're stupid and have nothing better to do. Awareness of the environment and of the homeostatic connection between internal and external is so intensely pleasurable that it is a magnet for your attention.

Just as your attention roots into the earth through the feet, it roots into the environment through the senses as well as through the skin all over your body. No longer are your senses thieves, robbing you of your attention, causing you to feel that the sensory world is the "other." Now the energy flow is two-way. It is a circular flow to and from the environment. You and the environment are intricately united.

The Illusion of Time

When you tried to remember your early life, you naturally tried to remember events—sequential activities in time. Now, perceiving as a child, you realize the folly of this method. BM does not remember in sequential time; it remembers in homeostatic relationships—that is, the balancing of energies.

Sequential time is a perspective of the mind. It is a method by which the mind stores information. BM stores its knowledge in the form of skill—the increasing ability to perform tasks. Your various skills are a testament to the memory of BM. Skill is a relationship or structure of feelings, while mind memory is a structure of thought.

The Form, with its emphasis on the feeling of energy patterns, pulls open the curtains hiding feeling memories. In the balancing of physical momentum and energy, you are reexperiencing the state of a child before time. The experience of sequential time shifts the memory process from BM to mind. In addition, it drastically alters the homeostatic processes, forcing you to connect with society rather than with nature. Once your behavior is regulated by time rather than by internal and external environmental conditions, your sensitivity is not needed. You only need to look at a clock to know what to do.

This is one way in which mind has gained power over the body. Time is an idea, a way of looking at things. It is a form of measurement between activities used to regulate a complex society. You make your activities conform to a standard time measurement for the sake of convenience. But rather than using time as a tool, you have used it as a substitute for sensitivity. You eat or sleep because it is a certain time. There is a Zen story: The student asked his teacher, "What is the essence of Zen?" His teacher replied, "When hungry, eat; when tired, sleep."

Time has become a reason for activity. If I were to say, "I have to go to the bathroom because it is twelve o'clock," you would think I was silly. But if I said, "I have to eat lunch because it is twelve o'clock," that might sound more reasonable. Yet it is just as silly.

Return of Feelings

During the Form you rebuild a repertoire of feelings. You notice all the various patterns of energy and how they feel. Then in your daily life, you notice when those same feelings arise again in particular situations. Perhaps there is a certain feeling associated with moments of self-doubt. Examining that feeling, you may find it consists of certain energy blockages and muscle tensions. By working on the physical level and letting go of the blockages and tensions, the behavior of self-doubt is dissolved.

Perhaps there is a certain feeling associated with embarrassment. There may be a rush of adrenalin and a resistance to the feelings within you. Perhaps someone has produced self-doubt in you by exposing something you feel to be negative. You fear that feeling; you don't want to have it. Embarrassment has the negative connotation of personal debasement.

To a T'ai-chi person, embarrassment is nothing more than a structure of internal feelings. You welcome that feeling and search within it for any problems such as energy blockages and tension. These you release. Rather than being more careful to hide your faults in the future, you look forward to the next experience of embarrassment to examine that feeling again. When it comes, you do not push it away; you welcome it, for it is part of you. The resistance against your own feelings is thus eliminated.

When such a feeling arises, you can relate it to other feelings that you experience in the Form. No longer will the feeling we call embarrassment be linked to mind—to the idea that you are a lesser person than someone else. This feeling will now be linked to all the other feelings and will be examined from the viewpoint of homeostasis, the balancing of energy. If it makes sense within this viewpoint, it will be incorporated into your feeling repertoire; if not, it will simply be let go. Your body will thus be returned to BM. The ability of another person to control your energy pattern through embarrassment or anger is eliminated.

When you learn the "language" of subconscious body feelings, you can understand your life more clearly. You can focus your attention down to the BM level of experience, the play of internal energies, and see where any imbalance exists. Through T'ai-chi techniques or an alteration in your external actions, you can rebalance the energy. You also become aware of how imbalances are caused and can learn to prevent them.

Further, you will become aware of the result of imbalances: ill health, changes of mood and behavior, etc. A particular feeling of imbalance will tell you that a particular aspect of your life needs to be dealt with. When I start feeling negative about the work that has to be done around the house, for example, it is usually because I haven't given myself time to relax. If I rush to catch up on my work, I will get more and more irritable until I get sick. In this case, sitting out in the back yard for an hour is the best long-term solution to maintain my health.

Use of the Mind

In this case, the thinking mind is cooperating with the homeostatic processes of the body. There is an open communication between the two and a common goal—the well-being of the person.

Mind may look into the future and realize that a particular course of action will benefit your well-being in the long run. BM relates how this course of action is affecting you now, minute to minute. The interplay between long-term and short-term well-being is a delicate matter. After all, that long-term benefit may never come, and meanwhile you may be suffering in the short term. If your mind is convinced that you must suffer in order to get to heaven, for example, then your entire life will be spent suffering. The mind can be convinced of anything, for it has only logic as its guide. Logic is a method of analyzing facts. Depending on its source of information, the mind can come to many conclusions.

It may sound perfectly logical that there is a God who is testing you to see if you deserve to get to heaven. But this logic isn't doing your biological organism any good. If your mind were to become sensitive enough to see the damage it sometimes causes you from its dependence on logic, it might start thinking along different lines. The mind is, after all, a tool to improve the well-being of the whole organism, not to destroy it. If it can see and understand the results of its decisions, it can gradually learn to improve its decision-making ability. Logic alone is not enough. The mind must be made aware of the effects of its actions on the health of the organism. In this way it will be part of the biofeedback mechanism of the body, the mechanism by which homeostasis works.

Going back to the example of driving a car, if you see your car moving too far to the right, you turn the wheel to make the car move back to the center of the lane. Sight is thus being used as a biofeedback system. Your whole being is filled with biofeedback mechanisms affecting your temperature, the chemical composition of your blood, how much food you ingest, your heart rate, breathing rate, etc.

It is a difficult lesson to learn that there are forces out there trying to separate your mind from your biofeedback system. The advertising industry is an obvious example. One salesman, putting two identical drinking glasses in front of me, told me that his job was to convince me that one glass was better than the other. In other words, his job was to fool me. There are many good talkers out there who can convince us of many things. Once our minds are disconnected from our biofeedback systems, they are helpless. They have no way of knowing what is going on.

During T'ai-chi classes the teacher discusses energy-pattern feelings. You gradually learn how your internal world is related to your external world, how this relationship was once severed to some extent and how to reconnect these two worlds. Once mind and BM are reconnected, you have two perspectives by which to understand your world. In one perspective, the "internal" world of the body and the "external" world of the senses are no longer separate. Your entire world is one ecological whole, ruled by the processes of balancing.

In the other perspective, that of separation of mind and BM, each part of your world can be observed and analyzed separately and distinctly. In this case mind is like an artist who stands back from his painting to see it from a distance. But from this vantage point he cannot reach over and put more paint on the canvas. To do that, he must again step close to the painting.

Your two perspectives are like this. Mind can step back and analyze but it cannot create. The minds of most people take still another tact. These artists walk right up to the canvas and stick their eyes one inch from the paint. They cannot see the whole picture, only the finest details. It is difficult for them to see how these details relate to each other.

Creativity lies in the realm of feeling memory. This is not a memory of events, but a memory of states of consciousness. The mind crystallizes one state of consciousness and allows you to function only within that particular state. But true creativity depends on going back to BM and remembering the feeling of other consciousness states. Each state of consciousness gives you certain powers. The development of modern technology has evolved from a deliberate structuring of our state of consciousness. And yet, with all the medical knowledge at our disposal, the general health of the average person has not improved. This shows that we need other powers besides technology to maintain our health. A change in perspective emphasizing balance and integration of yourself with your environment will be as effective in maintaining health as our present perspective is effective in developing technology.

While there may be contradictions between the two perspectives, BM is not uncomfortable with contradictions. It is the center of creativity and from this center sees each perspective as an artistic tool for improving your life. The differences between these tools allow them to be used for different purposes. Only when your attention is centered in BM can you use all your tools effectively.

Centering

Every balancing system is based on the principle of centering. The seesaw rests on a central fulcrum, allowing it to rock up and down. If the fulcrum were to be moved the slightest bit to one side, the seesaw would fall on one end.

Compasses work by having a magnetized needle-like piece of metal resting on a fulcrum. Freedom of movement in 360 degrees allows the needle to align itself with the earth's flow of magnetic energy. If the fulcrum were to be shifted slightly, the needle would fall on one end and cease to work.

The fulcrum empowers that which it balances by giving it freedom of movement. Within the body, the fulcrum point which empowers the homeostatic mechanism is the sense of an "optimal condition." The knowledge of BM consists of this innate sensing of the proper amount of sleep, eating, fasting, social activity, solitude, etc. BM may be thought of as the fulcrum point around which all your activities are balanced. If you rely too heavily on one aspect of yourself (such as thinking), your seesaw will fall down on one end. At any one time, of course, the body will be involved primarily in one or two activities. Balance within your life takes place over a span of time; you are balanced over the course of a day or a week.

Training in personal balance comes from the Form. The Form teaches you that there are two forces at work in your life. One force is maintaining the central fulcrum described above. Whenever you get too involved in a vigorous activity, for example, you feel a need for rest. After you have rested, there is the desire for play or work. This may be termed the "yin" force, or the stillness between two extremes, which tries to maintain a balance.

The "yang" force is that urge to move out from the center, the yearning for activity, for going to the extreme. With a balance of activity and stillness, the organism is in dynamic equilibrium, active yet balanced. "Dynamic equilibrium" is a term commonly used to describe living systems. It is a description of the homeostatic process. Equilibrium refers to balance and centering, while dynamic refers to activity and change.

If you can understand this principle in your life, you can achieve an "optimal state" biologically, emotionally, psychologically and spiritually. Far from being rigid, this is a fluid state, adjusting to the changing environment.

Balance of Internal and External Awareness

Interference with this dynamic equilibrium leads to distress and disease. An animal in the forest is at home with these principles. Its life is run by homeostasis. It is not smart enough to hurt itself. Yet the environment can hurt it. If there is a drought or disease, a fox or tiger may starve or fall ill. We humans have power over our environment. We can prevent drought and innoculate ourselves against disease. But our abilities to shield ourselves from environmental harm have been achieved at a sacrifice. Focusing on manipulating the external environment to achieve an optimal condition, we have become dull to our own internal homeostatic process.

Answers to the question, "Why aren't I happy?" are sought in manipulation of the external environment. Yet the principle of "optimal condition" does not depend on the external environment to a large extent. The body is able to reach a healthy condition in almost any environment. It is the enhancement of the body's sensitivity to balance and homeostasis which results in well-being and happiness.

Often, we tend to blame the people and conditions around us for our problems. This is because we have become addicted to external solutions. Our five senses have become thieves and robbed our biofeedback mechanisms of their energy. The seesaw between internal and external has become overbalanced on the side of external and has fallen down on that side. Thus, the entire organism suffers. The more we suffer, the more we look for solutions by placing weight on the external side, while the more appropriate solution would be to rebalance the seesaw by empowering our internal sensitivity. It is difficult for us to see how a lessening of attention to our external troubles will lead to their solution. It defies common sense. If we need more money, how can paying attention to our biofeedback mechanisms help?

The human organism exists on many levels and each must be taken care of. If we get off balance and concentrate on only one level, the entire organism is made impotent. The solution to any problem must begin with centering.

The Tan-tien

In the Form, you may ask why you are having problems with a certain movement. Your teacher will immediately pay attention to how you are centered. Is all your weight falling down through the center of your body? Are your movements centered in the Tan-tien? Are your turns centered around the spinal column? Within the Form are many centers of rotation, many fulcrums, the main one being the Tan-tien. The joints are also pivotal points.

By focusing your attention on movement around centers of balance, the attention shifts to the homeostatic mechanism and empowers this mechanism, resulting in the maintenance of optimal health. The balance/counterbalance of momentum in the Form is a teaching device to familiarize you with the type of skill involved in the homeostatic mechanism. Your attention focuses down to the most minute inner workings of the cells, organs, glands, nerves and muscles. You become as familiar with yourself as you are with your immediate external physical world.

Focused attention acts as a fulcrum, and it is a skill to know where to place that fulcrum. Whatever you pay a great deal of attention to will become a pivotal point around which your life will revolve. When two people pay a lot of attention to each other, for example, their lives begin to revolve around each other. If you pay attention to a particular belief system, your behavior begins to revolve around those beliefs. By sinking your attention in the Tan-tien, your behavior revolves around the homeostatic mechanism and thus around health.

The internal experience of the Form is that of swirls of momentum around the Tan-tien. This creates a biological gyroscope. A mechanical gyroscope is kept stable and centered by the spinning of a heavy central core. Within the body, the spinning of energy does the same thing biologically. Once your attention becomes familiar with these forces within your body, you can learn to coordinate them and combine their power.

In throwing a punch, for example, there are several movements at work. The first is the rotation of the body around the spinal column. The second is a shift of weight from the rear foot to the front. The third is a wave-like movement from the feet through the Tan-tien and out the fist. These various movements are aligned with each other through the medium of attention just as planetary bodies are aligned through the forces of gravity and momentum.

Central headquarters for this coordination is the center of the spider's web, the Tan-tien. This is the gearing mechanism through which all the forces of the body are interrelated. When you punch, you do not pay attention to the fist but to the Tan-tien. It feels as though a bolt of energy shoots up through the arm into the other person's body and then drains instantly back into the Tan-tien. Since this is a balance/counterbalance system, another bolt of energy is felt to shoot from the Tan-tien through the legs and into the ground. A punch is felt as a counterbalanced release of energy.

Gradually, as we become more sensitive, we experience more and more homeostatic mechanisms which are centered in the Tan-tien. Every level of being—molecular, cellular and organic—is coordinated by the Tan-tien. The relationships among members within the same level (the individual cells, for example) are also coordinated by the Tan-tien. The Tan-tien is the center of harmony among all your individual parts. By sinking your attention into this level, you are placing the body's fulcrum at the center of harmony and thus empowering it.

Note that no particular philosophy or belief system is needed. Thoughts need not be involved at all; in fact, attention must be drained from mind to add more to the Tan-tien. Studying spiritual philosophy or religion often makes you no more spiritual or happy. T'ai-chi-Ch'uan is a very concrete and visible method of achieving harmony within yourself. It brings vague longings for a better life into concrete terms.

Holographic Attention

We believe that human beings are powerful creatures, fully capable of living happy, fulfilling lives and of curing themselves of their ills. It is the perception of ourselves as pitiful, helpless creatures which causes our troubles. When I speak of being aware of all the countless cells of the body and how they interact with each other, many people would think this absurd, that a human being is incapable of such a feat of concentration. There are trillions of cells. Most of us can hardly concentrate on three things at the same time. How can we concentrate on trillions of things as the same time?

First, all those parts obviously *are* coordinated. If we look at the planet as a whole, we can see that, ecologically, all of its parts are coordinated. On a galactic scale, all the movements of the planets and stars are coordinated. But our minds find this hard to understand because the thinking mind works linearly, one thought at a time. Yet in its focused attention on only one thing at a time, the mind is powerful. The balance between universal concentration (BM) and singular concentration (mind) is taught in the Form.

Universal concentration is called "holographic." This term is based on the workings of a three-dimensional holographic picture. Put in simple terms, a hologram is a flat plate containing circular patterns. Each tiny section of the plate contains enough information about the original scene to reproduce that scene. Such a reproduction is effected by shining laser light through the plate. But if only a section of the plate is used, the resulting picture will not appear three-dimensional, because each section contains information showing the original scene from only one angle. The entire plate is needed to reproduce a three-dimensional picture.

The holographic model has been expanded to describe the manner in which the human nervous system works. Any piece of information, it is theorized, is stored by the entire nervous system. A thought structure or state of consciousness is really reflective of the entire state of the nervous system at that time. Any one nerve or set of nerves can only contain one perspective or angle of that information or state of consciousness. When a thought erupts in the consciousness, it is not because only one nerve is active and the rest are shut down. The entire nervous system is alive and functioning at all times. The mind's task is to filter out the entire perceptual picture except for one little piece. Holographic attention is what we achieve when the filter is removed. Thus BM is continually functioning but is mostly hidden from view by mind, which does not create anything; it merely selectively blocks what is already there. When mind is dropped and we sink our attention into BM, we realize that all our trillions of parts are in touch with each other through BM.

This model of consciousness reveals a clue for another field—quantum physics, which deals with the behavior of subatomic particles. One of the enigmas of quantum physics is that sometimes these particles behave as if they were smart, as if they knew what was going on somewhere else. Quantum physics emerged from Newtonian physics, which considered the universe to be composed of objects knocking into each other. Every interaction could be predicted well into the future by applying Newton's laws of motion.

On the subatomic level, however, the world does not seem to act exactly as it does up here. Quantum physics can predict the behavior of a group of particles, but not of an individual particle.

There is a tendency for a particle to change its behavior when a distant environment that has nothing to do with the particle is changed. It is as though someone placed a call to the particle and said, "Guess what, they just built a new skating rink." The particle suddenly changes its plans and decides to go skating. "Synchronicity" is the name given to an unexpected connection between two seemingly unrelated events.

We can see from the example of the holographic model for human functioning how seemingly unrelated events can be linked. How can all the trillions of activities within the body be coordinated? Through the Tan-tien, the harmonizing part of ourselves, seat of the individual Tao. The more our attention is centered there, the more we empower that harmony and the healthier we become.

Harmony and Freedom

Let's take this a step further. On an ecological level there is harmony among all living and nonliving things on this planet. Imagine each plant and animal with its trillions of microscopic interactions. How much more powerful a harmonizing center must be to create harmony on a planetary level. And how much beyond that on solar, galactic and universal levels!

You can gain an insight into these magnificent mechanisms by concentrating on your own Tan-tien. When you can release your own thinking mind and experience the totality of yourself at one glance, you will have experienced, in miniature, the universal BM. The Form is a technique through which to experience this. It is designed to be learned by BM. At first, your mind tries to learn it and continually falls short of its expectations. Only when the Form has become internalized, when it is played out by BM, can it be done correctly.

A musician works the same way. He is not concentrating on each finger, but on the feeling of the musical piece he is playing. The fingers turn into auditory form what the musician is concentrating on. It is as if each finger is intelligent and needs only the concentration of the musician on the song in his imagination to work properly. One end of an imaginary stretched rubber band is attached to the imagination of the musician. The other end is attached to the fingers. Attention shoots through the Tan-tien both ways and the song is played. If you are a musician, consider this and see if it applies. The musician must actually "let go" of his fingers in order for them to work properly. They must be allowed to dance freely by themselves. The balance between control of the fingers and giving them their freedom is a central issue in the quality of the resultant music.

The same is true within your body. While there is harmony among all parts, there is freedom as well; your proper functioning requires a balance between these two forces. On a planetary scale, this is true as well. Look at our own species. We have developed a lot of independence, but unless this independence is balanced with harmony with the rest of nature, the whole system will collapse; it will fall on one end like the seesaw. Human culture as a whole is reflective of the state of consciousness of each individual. With more and more individuals going through a rebalancing with T'ai-chi-Ch'uan and other such systems, the human race as a whole will be rebalanced. The yang aspect, that of reaching for the extremes, will be lessened in favor of the yin, that of remaining centered. By getting involved in T'ai-chi-Ch'uan, people will not only add to this centering process but will also be developing a conceptual framework by which to understand the changes which are coming to our society. In this way, they will not be disturbed by those changes, but be able to adapt to and take advantage of them.

Lessons of Centering

By describing the principle on which nature works, that of balance, I hope to explain why a rebalancing in favor of BM will solve many of our individual and world-wide problems. The song of T'ai-chi is a harmonious life and a harmonious world. While we begin by learning scales, breath control, how to hold the instrument, etc. (the Form), the eventual goal is to play a tune (to apply T'ai-chi to our daily lives).

Let's examine one of the basic beginning teachings of the Form to see how it can eventually be used to enhance your everyday life.

During the Form, the feet are usually placed in a position described as the T'ai-chi stance, at the corners of an imaginary square formed on the ground, the sides of which are one shoulder-length in size. The front foot is pointed straight ahead and contains seventy percent of the weight of the body. At the rear corner, the back foot is pointed at a forty-five-degree angle and contains thirty percent of the weight. Both knees are bent and face inward so that if a line were drawn through each, those lines would intersect about three feet in front of your body. Your hips and chest are relaxed as usual. In this position, the weight of the body should fall directly down into the center of that imaginary square formed on the ground. This is a very stable position, but it is easy for you to step out because most of your weight is on one foot; you are not double-weighted.

As you step about, the base within which your weight must fall moves with you. If you were to stand on one leg, then the base would be narrowed to that one leg; your weight would have to fall straight through the leg which remains on the ground for you to remain stable. The raised leg might be stretched out forward while the body leans slightly backward. In this case, the outstretched leg counterbalances the leaning body, and the overall effect is a centering of the weight through the leg which remains on the ground.

The weight should not only be lined up with the center of the square but should be kept low. If your center of weight, or "center of gravity," is too high, you will fall off balance. With a low center of gravity, you are like a child's punching toy, weighted at the bottom. No matter how hard it is pushed or punched, the toy always rights itself.

Too often, we learn to stand in an exaggerated posture with chest puffed out and an unnaturally large curve in the small of the back. This brings the center of gravity up too high and results in a balance similar to an upside-down bowling pin. The slightest nudge will push that pin over. With your weight close to the ground and centered, you can maintain your root.

In this simple teaching of balance and coordination lie clues to the methods of developing better mental and emotional balance and coordination. In T'ai-chi-Ch'uan we speak of not "getting thrown" easily. This refers to the development of a low center of gravity, to centering your weight and developing your root. The moment you begin to feel off balance, your immediate response is to sink, center and root. A student who responds this way automatically on a physical plane will respond the same way emotionally. Rather than being "thrown" emotionally and raising the emotional center of gravity (getting upset), you will immediately seek that clear, calm, grounded place within you and center yourself. From this calm center, you will notice more clearly how you are being affected by the outside circumstance and yet, although some parts of you may be triggered by that circumstance, your attention remains seated in the calm center. In this way you can see how others are trying to manipulate you and how to avoid that manipulation.

A Test of Centeredness

I once visited the open house of one of the students of an Indian guru. He was attempting to recruit new members. His method consisted of first implanting the seeds of doubt within the visitor by suggesting that there was sadness at different times in the visitor's life. This shouldn't be, he said. There was never any sadness among his students. Gradually he gave the visitors the impression that their lives were a mess. While undermining self-confidence in the visitors, he acted in an exaggerated self-confident manner himself. That was his second technique. Many people are looking for a strong personality to lead them and solve all their problems. His third technique was that of reward-punishment. He reacted angrily when we responded in a manner he disapproved of and positively when we responded well. In this manner, he hoped to make us want to please him.

I noticed that his regular students were very meek (which is understandable), so when the guru suggested that we do some "T-grouping" (acting through situations in our lives by doing a little drama), I said that I had difficulty dealing with people who yell at me and criticize me. The guru then told his students to sit around me, yell and criticize me. They were unable to. They had been made so meek by their teacher that they could not even make-believe they were being aggressive. I was hoping to teach the students something by this.

Soon after, the guru tried to convince me to join his group and hand over my bank account to them.

"Were you planning to visit us, learn from our teachings and not pay for it?" he asked angrily.

"That's exactly what I expected to do," I answered.

"What's the matter, don't you trust us?" he asked.

"No."

"Do you think we want to hurt you or cheat you?"

"No."

"Then do you trust us?"

"No."

"If you don't think we mean you any harm, then why don't you trust us?"

"I don't trust your competence."

At that point, I was accused of being "slippery." My intention was, as a visitor, to actually become a teacher to his students and show them a path out of intimidation. The game we played with each other was obvious. He tried to undermine my self-confidence. I tried to remain centered and clear. I later verified my opinion of the man by contacting others who knew him well.

I enjoy visiting situations in which someone tries to control and brainwash me. I feel it sharpens my centering skills as much as the game of Push Hands sharpens the physical centering skills. In each case, your partner in the game tries to push you off balance. Your partners in "real" life are the people and situations you meet.

Living a Centered Life

To me, it's not enough to understand the principles of a philosophy; you must practice it in your life. This is why T'ai-chi-Ch'uan gives you very concrete, physical metaphors for all the philosophy. We don't try to brainwash anyone, for we do not consider the teacher to be "better" than the student. Each is a creature of nature, a product of billions of years of evolution. As such, each is already enlightened, already part of this great life force. The teacher merely gives the students various tools with which to develop their abilities.

This is not to imply that the Chinese way is better than the Indian way. There are many ways, and each is suited to the different temperaments and needs of the students. Even within T'ai-chi-Ch'uan, there are manipulative teachers and students. On the teacher's part, there is the element of competition, the feeling that "my T'ai-chi is better than someone else's." For such a teacher to remain centered would mean recognizing this tendency within himself but not allowing it to take over his behavior. He must not allow that competitive tendency to grab his attention and pull it from the center, upsetting his calmness. If he feels negative toward other teachers, how can he learn from them? On the other hand, when he sees such a fault, he must not try to push it away, for then it will grab his attention as well, this time in a negative manner. Not following it, not pushing it away, the T'ai-chi teacher will simply let go of it, remaining free to choose his course of action, remaining free to choose the distribution of his attention. When I meet a competitive teacher, I ask him his advice about T'ai-chi, so that he can feel more relaxed. In this way, we can have true two-way communication and avoid building walls between us.

But even students can be coercive. Naturally, you like to feel that your teacher is the best T'ai-chi teacher in the world. Since you are a student of the best teacher, this naturally means you are a top student. It's the old ego sneaking in through the back door. By worshipping your master, you pat yourself on the back, in addition to feeling that you are getting your money's worth in class.

Among martial artists in general, there is competition as to which style is the most effective. I have not yet heard one student who didn't feel his style was the best! Most spiritual and martial arts systems speak of humility; surely all students have heard this term. Well, sometimes they even compete with each other over how humble they are! In one school, affectionately known as Pretentiousness Unlimited, the teacher refuses to do Push Hands with other teachers unless they study with him for three years first!

So the world of T'ai-chi-Ch'uan is not immune from many of the failings of other systems. Yet I find a great deal of friendliness, mutual cooperation and a down-to-earth feeling. You just have to "choose your friends" in T'ai-chi as you would in general.

Many people, whatever their philosophy, have lost their center, or perspective. A particular attitude or manner of behavior has captured their attention and they have forgotten what it is like to be simple and straight-forward. While reaching out for the shinies, the glitter, they have forgotten the joy of simple sharing and caring among friends. At times I catch myself going for the glitter (or others catch me at it). The first sign that I'm doing so is that I no longer enjoy simple things—cutting the hedges, cooking an omelet, kissing, etc. I am off center, off balance. My seesaw has fallen down. Then I spend a great deal of effort trying to move that seesaw around when all I really have to do is to recenter the fulcrum (my attention). The next sign that I'm off center is that I feel upset and physically weak. Finally, I actually get sick. Learning to center yourself saves you a lot of trouble in life.

T'ai-chi-Ch'uan uses a language in its physical aspect that is readily adaptable to psychological and emotional levels. Such terms as "centering" can be applied to every aspect of our lives, as I just attempted to show. This makes it easy for students, when encountering difficult situations, to adapt a technique from the Form or Push Hands for use in their everyday lives.

There is a Zen saying, "When you walk, walk. When you sit, sit. Just don't wobble." This is another description of the quality of a centered person taken from an allied system. Among American Indians there is a similar saying, "Walk in balance on the Earth Mother" (Sun Bear of the Bear Tribe).

In T'ai-chi-Ch'uan, this is best exemplified by the turns on one leg. These turns are really spins, with only the ball or heel of one foot touching the ground. Your entire body rotates 180 or 360 degrees, then stops instantly. If you are the slightest bit off center, you will wobble and fall over.

The Center of Belief

Even the mind, the thinking process, needs centering. Notice the way in which scientific theories have changed over the past few hundred years. Each generation has its own explanations and produces its own proofs and technologies. Then the next generation comes up and proclaims the old theories invalid. In my own science training I was taught that by definition a theory was correct "if it worked."

Recently I spoke to one of my classes about atomic theories. "One version of the nature of matter says that most of those cinderblocks you're sitting on is empty space. Less than 1/10 of one percent is actual 'stuff.' Yet I know of no one who has fallen through a cinderblock. The mind must have its beliefs and those beliefs are its centering; they are its power. When you fully believe something, then you can act. If you believe that a cinderblock is solid, you can act to sit on it. If you weren't sure, you would wobble; you would hesitate."

The entire set of beliefs of a particular mind are its centering, and the life of that person revolves around them. They define the power of that person. But as a T'ai-chi student, you cannot afford to let your power be defined by your beliefs. Those beliefs, to a large extent, were programmed into you by society. By allowing your power to be defined by your beliefs, you give your power over to this programming. Then how can you be truly creative?

A scientist doesn't allow his power to be defined by his beliefs either. He allows it to be defined by the results of experimentation. (And even then he realizes that it is still safe to sit on a cinderblock.) A scientist can trace the history of the structure of belief by tracing various scientific experiments and their results throughout history. How many of us can trace the history of our belief system?

A T'ai-chi student does not succumb to the lure of belief. Belief is seen as a tool of centering, and the value of that tool is assessed in terms of "does it work?" rather than "is it true?" When a teacher tells you to breathe in through the feet, it is senseless to argue that you can only breathe through the nose or mouth. On the other hand, it would be just as inappropriate for the teacher to say, "Breathe in *as if* you were breathing through the feet." For you to gain power, you must be able to use beliefs as you use tools. A carpenter does not say, "Turn that screw *as if* you had a screwdriver in your hand." Unless you really have a screwdriver, that screw will not get turned. Unless you really believe you are breathing in through your feet, your progress will be impeded. Yet, you also believe that you breathe in through your nose. Each belief is a tool, to be used at the proper time. One belief does not counteract another, just as a screwdriver does not counteract a hammer.

It is a lack of understanding of this way of using ideas as tools that has led to a misinterpretation of ancient texts. (More on this in another chapter.) These texts are manuals of such tools and how to use them, but unless they are read by someone familiar with such tools, they are meaningless. Imagine a civilization a thousand years from now finding a copy of the periodic table of elements, upon which modern chemistry is based. Without knowledge of the science of chemistry, the periodic table is nothing more than scratches of ink on paper. While the future civilization may have a thorough knowledge of chemistry, their basic concepts may be so different from ours that the arrangement of elements on the table will not give them a single clue to its meaning.

Imagery

Our imagery of the composition of our world has been developed over thousands of years. A civilization which uses a different imagery is not necessarily "wrong" unless you feel that our civilization has the monopoly on truth. The imagery presented to you in this book is not meant to compete with any other "truth." It is offered to empower you—to provide powerful tools to improve your health, physically, emotionally, psychologically and spiritually. By learning the dynamics of a system based on an understanding of such tools, you may investigate other systems to analyze the imagery of those systems. In this way, you can find tools for living everywhere you search.

The issue of imagery is such a vast topic that it really requires an entire volume itself. On an everyday level, your own self-image has a large influence on your behavior. You have certain impressions as to who you are and how you act, and your behavior tends to follow your self-image. A large part of your social interactions are centered around maintaining your self-image—your opinions, capabilities, qualities, etc. Your self-image is what "places" you in your social world. The attempt to create a good image of ourselves in the eyes of others is what keeps the fashion industry in business. But some people will argue that they don't care what others feel about them. It is only their opinion of themselves that matters.

In T'ai-chi, we take another tack and use the process of imagery as a form of play. Recognizing the connection between imagery and behavior, we concentrate on various images to see how they affect the Form.

For example, you may concentrate on your memories of tigers stalking prey from movies you have seen. Letting go of your self-image, you replace your self-awareness with that of the tiger's image and try to act like a tiger within the confines of the specific movements of the Form. But it will not work if you are a *person* acting like a tiger. The awareness of yourself as a person must be dropped as much as possible, leaving only the structure of the Form to contain the tiger. To let go of yourself is the basic skill involved in using imagery.

Yet, if you are gone, who is doing the Form? BM is doing the Form and it doesn't care which self is on tap at any particular time. A self is a style superimposed on the natural flow of forces. Whether the Form is done in one style or another is of little consequence to BM. By practicing various styles of the Form, you are practicing different styles of self-image. No longer is your self-image controlled by the opinions of others or even by your own opinions. It is a product of your skill—of BM. You, that is, your self-image, become an artistic creation of BM and are no longer at anyone's mercy.

In the Long Island School of T'ai-chi-Ch'uan, each student practices at least eight such style Forms. Each is composed of the same specific movements and yet each looks quite different from the others and teaches different qualities.

1. *Standard Form*

We begin with the standard Form (the "yang" short Form), to which we return between learning each of the following Forms. The standard Form is devoid of exaggeration, simple, crisp, relaxed, even and flowing. As we learn each of the additional styles, we incorporate a bit of each into the standard Form. Within three years or so, the standard Form has become enriched with many qualities from the others. While it is still simple and not exaggerated, it has acquired a great deal of "substance."

2. *Slanting Form*

As the name implies, the body is used in a slanting, seesaw fashion to experiment with the principle of balance/counterbalance. This is taught while the students are learning Push Hands and teaches them to angle off the pressure which their partners are using to push them over.

3. *Old Man Form*

This Form is conducted as if the student were very weak. Movements are kept to a minimum and steps are small. This is useful when the student is actually sick and weakened. More important, it teaches the student that the development of internal power is a matter of concentration and relaxation and does not require a lot of physical movement. While doing Push Hands, it is essential to focus concentration on the flow of momentum and the relationship of the balance between the two bodies, and not on the hands and arms. Doing the Form as a weak old man tends to take attention from the external and bring it within the body. It also emphasizes giving up dramatic movements, which have no place in the Form.

4. *Snake Form*

This is a low, slinky, elastic Form. The body continually compresses into the legs and then releases. The arms move about in a snake-like fashion. Snake Form emphasizes the elasticity of all parts of the body and builds strength in the legs. It is practiced when the student begins to learn Kung-Fu (fighting). Also emphasized is focusing the attention totally on what lies ahead of you. The body almost seems to be pulled forward by the attention coming out of the eyes. The body feels like a coiled spring, always on the verge of being released. The steps are long and teach the student to step in close to the sparring partner while maintaining a very low stance. Snake Form also teaches evasiveness, so that the student may weave in and out between the partner's punches and kicks.

5. *Extended or Monkey Form*

This Form emphasizes bending the top of the body into extreme positions and yet retaining complete control over balance. It is a playful Form, always dancing just on the outer edge of being in balance. It builds the muscles of the hips and lower back to prevent the ripping of those muscles due to the rapid body movements of fighting. T'ai-chi-Ch'uan fighting emphasizes weaving in and out between the punches and kicks, so extremely rapid body movement is essential. For Push Hands, this Form develops the body's ability to move out of the way of a push rapidly.

6. *Closed Eyes Form*

Rather than being a specific Form, this is the standard Form done with closed eyes. Its purpose is to bring the attention within the body to balancing and flows of momentum. It is done when students are ready to develop skills in dealing with internal energy (chi). Previously, students depended to a large extent on their sense of sight to maintain balance. Now, with closed eyes, they are dependent on their sense of energy.

7. *Breathing Forms*

When students are ready to learn Chi-Gung (the teaching of how to use internal energy), Breathing Forms are taught. Again, this is the standard Form (now enriched by the others) with specific breathing techniques. Long ago, students have learned specific breathing for the Form, that is, which movements require an inbreath and which require an outbreath, but this is different. At this point, students are ready to handle large quantities of energy. Their tensions and energy blockages have largely been dissolved. Their competitive natures have been resolved to some extent. Their self-images have ceased to absorb so much of their attention. At this point they have become interested in using their abilities for healing purposes and for the general betterment of those around them. The benefits of living a simple life have been made clear. Glitter and clever thoughts have ceased to snare their attention.

Without these developments, the use of large amounts of power could be dangerous. Qualities effective in the business world would be quite the opposite in their personal lives. As much power as they generate is as much power as they must release; power must flow through them. Any attempt to store energy may result in injury to the students, just as too much pressure in a water pipe may burst the pipe. Breathing Forms teach students how to connect their internal energy with the energy of the environment.

In the first breathing Form, students breathe in from the earth and out through the top of the head. They breathe out down the body and legs, into the earth. This takes place as they are doing the standard Form. Their concentration is going up and down with the breath. The effect is that of an energy pump, building greater and greater energy pressure with each movement. Yet there is a release valve at the top of the head and at the bottoms of the feet for excess pressure.

Eventually the goal is to do what is generally referred to as *the* Breathing Form. It is a very difficult Form to describe. In this Form the self-image is dropped, as in the previous Forms. Replacing the self-image is an image of the breath, with all its qualities (pressure of the diaphragm, speed of breathing, depth of breath, etc.). The varying quality of the breathing controls the movements. Breathing actually becomes as influential on physical behavior as thinking is to the average person. If you doubt this, notice how influential your breathing is when you first wake up in the morning. Notice any connections between your breathing, dream imagery and your physical movements in bed. Most of us are not aware of the importance of correct breathing in our lives.

8. *Wispy Figure Form*

The self-image is replaced by the image of a wispy, mist-like human figure. (This is done with eyes closed.) By manipulating the figure in our imagination, our actual physical movements are controlled. This is not too odd to those who consider thoughts to be a product of imagination. If thoughts can control our movements, why not other forms of imagination? And eventually, why not learn to connect all aspects of imagination to our lives? Imagination is creativity. If we connect creativity to our lives, our lives will become powerful. That, of course, is the purpose of the Wispy Figure Form. Rather than having our lives controlled by thoughts alone, we now bring other powers of our being into the picture. Power over our lives is then shared by all the different parts of ourselves.

9. *Chakra Forms*

"Chakras" are centers of power within the spinal column. Each system, from China and Europe to the Americas and India, has its explanation of chakras. To each chakra is ascribed control of specific parts of our bodies. To describe the personal experience of Chakra Forms, I will ask for a "willing suspension of disbelief" on your part, a term borrowed from anthropology. As to what is happening scientifically, I can only guess.

A beam of chi is extended from a specific chakra to the ground a few feet in front of you. This beam acts as a controlling rod, connected to all the energies in your body. The energies within your body then interact with the energies of that chakra. You are developing a sort of coiled mainspring of power within each chakra which, when released, will gradually put the body through the Form. The connection of the chakra to the ground is to support the body, as the muscles are all relaxed to the greatest degree possible. It feels as if the beam of chakra energy is supporting the weight of the body. Actually, it is the muscles which are doing so, but this imagery allows the muscles to relax to a great degree.

The purpose of the Chakra Forms is to bring the chakras into participation with the activities of the body. These chakras are points at which the external energies of the environment connect with the body's energies. It is essential that the chakras be "turned on." The "beam of energy" of the Chakra Forms may be thought of as an image, something from the imagination. Yet, to the students, it feels as real as a table or a tree. They begin to see that what they assume to be "real" and what they assume to be "imaginary" are really only a matter of choice.

Imagery Forms train us in the making of such choices. In a very real sense, they train us to create our own world. If you have ever asked two people to report on an accident both of them witnessed, you know how flaky reality can sometimes be. The "final Form" the student develops is a little of this Form and a little of that, all added to the standard Form. The Form of T'ai-chi-Ch'uan is a metaphor for your life. Imagery Forms, therefore, train you to create your own life by centering your attention on your creative power.

Energy Patterns

The perspective of energy patterns, as taught by the various styles of the Form, is an extremely valuable one in daily life. This perspective is present in all religions, philosophies and sciences. By reading a description of this perspective in T'ai-chi terms, see if you can apply it to your own philosophy and daily life. If you watch children play, you will find they play-act different roles, making believe they are firefighters, astronauts or Luke Skywalker. BM is very active in children. It loves to experience. From engaging in various experiences, it learns and grows.

A powerful way for BM to grow is for it to come in contact with people who possess a quality that it needs to develop. Perhaps a person lacks self-confidence, grounding or physical strength. BM knows that these lacks stem from a problem in the energy pattern of that person. It is from this energy pattern, this individual Tao, that the characteristics of the emotions, mind and physical body arise. Due to the particular senses we possess, we do not perceive this underlying energy pattern, but only its products. Our attention is so centered on the senses that we pay little attention to the experience of BM, which is the experience of this energy. But from BM's vantage point, the situation might appear like this: We are composed of innumerable eddies and currents of energy flows, but from some of the experiences we have in our lives, these flows may be altered, injuring us in some way.

Healing the Energy Pattern

An easy way to correct an imbalance in the energy flow is to come into close contact with another person whose energy flow in that particular area resembles the type of pattern you need to improve your condition. By coming into close contact (physically or emotionally) with this person, your own energy flow will be influenced by his or hers and may return to its healthy condition.

This is the basis of many relationships. The feeling of love that arises is actually a feeling of need to repair an injured energy pattern. Rather than developing a fluid pattern which can heal itself by changing, you want a person with a well pattern near you, so you won't actually have to change yourself. This is not really love and will not last.

By practicing style Forms, this situation becomes unnecessary. First of all, your energy pattern is kept loose and fluid and generally will not be warped by the negative influences of society. Second, if there is a warping, you can more easily correct it by yourself. If worse comes to worse, you can visualize the correct pattern and adapt it to your own. If you meet a person with a counterbalancing pattern, you can allow the influence of that person's pattern to change your own in a matter of a few days or even hours.

Another reason BM tries to come into contact with other patterns is for the sheer joy of it. Even without a specific problem, when BM comes into contact with someone it enjoys, it attempts to imitate that pattern to bring that joy within itself. Relationships based on this function of BM usually last. However, this may result in your self-image being replaced by the image of the person you try to imitate, just as you replace your self-image with that of a tiger or a monkey to do the style Forms. There is a problem with this, for even though there are positive qualities in the other person, there may be negative qualities as well. As a T'ai-chi-Ch'uan student, you must learn to distinguish between the two, allowing only those patterns you want to adapt to come through.

Now this may seem like a simple psychological explanation couched in mystical terms, but there is a difference. We believe that the energy pattern affects physical structure, emotions, thoughts and even the relationship of the individual to his environment. The changing of your pattern will cause changes in the way in which future events unfold. You can see that retaining control over this pattern is the central issue of personal power. If you feel another person has a certain power, you will try to detect what aspect of his pattern gives him this power and adapt it to your own. Skill at music may be a power you admire but you find hard to learn. Fast reflexes may be a problem for you in your tennis game. You may be shy around people. Observations of the energy patterns of others will help you. Of course, these observations are not visual, but made through the sense of energy which is developed in T'ai-chi-Ch'uan.

If you are very sensitive to such patterns, you may be able to pick up a valuable quality merely by seeing someone interact with other peole or even just walk by. Without even knowing the person, you can bring this pattern into yourself and try it on for size, so to speak, to see what changes it produces in you. T'ai-chi-Ch'uan students are people watchers and experience great joy from feeling the consciousness of others. The American Indian saying, "Don't judge a person until you walk a mile in his moccasins," is well heeded.

Through this process, T'ai-chi teachers can better understand their students and provide a more individualized teaching for each one. Your teacher can sense problems with your energy pattern and correct it. Yet the teacher does not interfere with your individuality. The artistic manner in which you have developed your own pattern must be respected. The teacher is there to provide help when you get stuck or when your pattern is damaged. He also teaches you artistic means of playing with and using your energy pattern.

In shamanistic societies, usually small tribes, patterns of energy are termed "power animals." The shaman acquires several of these power animals for use, mainly in healing. In other systems they may be termed "spirits." These are externalizations of a natural internal process. People who are resistant to changes in their patterns may externalize such changes and imagine them as separate entities which are possessing them. In T'ai-chi-Ch'uan, we accept such changes as part of our natural growth and attempt to influence them to proceed in a positive way.

Harmonizing Internal and External Energy

Our energy patterns are connected to the energy of the natural environment. When there are changes in the environment, they affect our own patterns. Seasonal changes, even weather changes, have their effects. Many cultures perform rituals at the onset of the seasons to prepare their people for the changes they are about to experience. (Taoism is one of those cultures.) If you are not prepared, the change of the energy pattern in the environment may come as a shock and your health may suffer. Such rituals are really healing rituals in the sense that they maintain health by maintaining a harmony between the individual and planetary energy systems.

Imagine your predicament as a person whose entire energy pattern is intricately connected to the energy pattern of the planet. On the one hand, you are extremely sensitive to the environment and would not do anything to destroy or interfere with it. On the other hand, you are connected to great sources of power. How can you use that power if you have to be so careful not to disrupt your environment? By practicing the alteration of your own pattern, you can determine how it affects the planetary energy surrounding you. Alterations in your pattern send ripples throughout your immediate environment. In this way, you can gain the knowledge and understanding necessary for you to influence your own life, the environment and the relationship of the two in a positive way. American Indians, for example, will thank the soul of a deer they kill as food. Life is sacred, but to feed their own families they must kill other animals. Yet their show of respect for that deer maintains their sacred feeling for life.

One who works with the energy perspective in this way is like a musician. The musician plays his instrument (energy pattern) within a vast world-wide orchestra of other creatures who are all playing their own instruments. While he must remain in harmony with the other players, he is certainly free to alter the quality of his playing to express his artistic feelings. Unfortunately, our modern society has lost this energy perspective, not to mention the actual feelings of energy. So we continue destroying the environment and disrupting the great harmony. As an individual you can make a great contribution to reversing this situation by bringing natural harmony back into your own life. If you can sense how the pattern of energy within you is a balancing system, you will be better able to keep your own life in balance.

Furthermore, it is easy to see how unwanted habits such as cigarette smoking are difficult to overcome merely by trying to force yourself to stop. These habits are ingrained in the energy pattern. By working directly with the energy, such habits are more easily dropped. Working with the energy pattern is a more efficient lever by which to make changes in your life.

To someone just beginning T'ai-chi-Ch'uan, though, the idea of energy patterns may seem far-fetched. Yet the exercises are designed to make the experience of chi (internal energy) so vivid that eventually you will notice it. The principle of energy flow is central to T'ai-chi-Ch'uan. I was once teaching a T'ai-chi-Ch'uan teacher the advanced stages of this art, which require working with energy. Surprisingly, he refused to believe there was such a thing as internal energy and kept insisting that I was deluding myself. After two years of this, I gave up and we stopped practicing together. Three weeks later, he called me and told me about a strange feeling he was having. When he described it to me, I realized that he had finally experienced chi.

T'ai-chi-Ch'uan teaches the artistic skill of playing with the interaction of internal and external energy. Once this interaction is experienced directly, rather than by simply reading about it, you know that you need have no more confusion in your life. You have opened the back of the watch and seen the complex mechanism inside. You have taken a peek behind the scenes and witnessed what makes life tick. Then confusion and self-doubt will no longer be able to trip you up.

CHAPTER 3
PUSH HANDS

Push Hands is a game. It is a game of tossing energy back and forth between two people with the aim of throwing your partner off balance. The energy used in this game is physical momentum generated by waves of motion, from the feet up through the arms, by the turning of the body and by shifting the weight between the rear and front foot.

Perhaps "push" is not an appropriate word, for it implies muscular tension in the arms and hands. In this game the arms and hands act as cushiony shock absorbers. It is the momentum itself, generated by the motion of the body and the flow of internal energy through the arms, which effects the push. As you attempt to push your partner off balance, you are also neutralizing the force of your partner, who is trying to push you at the same time. As the energy of your partner comes your way, you move out of the way of that energy by shifting your weight, turning your body and angling the top of it. In this way, you are like a balloon floating in the air which is hard to grasp because it offers no resistance. Your feet, though, are rooted in the ground like a child's punching toy which always rights itself because it is weighted at the bottom. You are like a sapling which is flexible above ground but deeply rooted below. The strongest winds cannot break it, for it is soft and yielding; nor can the wind uproot it, because it is firmly rooted.

Yielding

The Push Hands game is designed to teach lessons which seem illogical. In our everyday world it seems that power and control are inseparable. Large countries build their military power to control smaller countries. Some people are afraid to fall in love because the person they love will have power over them and be able to control them.

You learn in Push Hands that the more control you give to your partner, the less power he has. This is a great secret which when fully understood gives you great personal power and can completely change your life.

To understand this principle, you must first visualize the mechanical work-ings of the game. Two people stand facing each other in elongatged T'ai-chi stances (feet at the corners of a rectangle). The posture is relaxed, as in the Form, and the forearms or hands of the partners are touching. Their bodies weave backward and forward, to the left and right, turning on their axes. As partner #1 attempts to push #2 off balance, #2 allows his body to float in the direction it is being pushed. If #2 should resist the push of #1 at any point, #1 will feel this resistance as a stiffening and will then have something firm to push against. Each partner is sensing such resistances or tensions within the other, for only when they are felt can one push the other over. Otherwise each partner will just be pushing against something that feels like a wet noodle.

The ability to sense every little movement of your partner and to allow your body to drift away from it is the first Push Hands essential. Your partner may change the direction and strength of the push each second and attempt to twist your body into awkward positions, yet your body must be fluid and flexible enough to drift away from the push. This is called "external neutralization." In this manner, you are giving control of your movements to your partner. You are neutral, not trying to manipulate the movements. You respond to the will, the intention of your partner, and flow with it. Yet your partner is not able to con-trol you with his will. By offering no resistance, you have dissipated his will and control. By remaining rooted in the earth, you stay centered in your position. While soft and yielding on the outside, you are firm on the inside, not at all like a leaf blown about by the wind. By following your partner and drifting away in this manner, there should never be more than four ounces of pressure between the arms or hands which are touching each other.

If you are not well versed in Push Hands, the game can be maddening. When you first try it, you feel very powerful because your opponent feels soft, and soft-ness is usually equated with weakness. So you push and shove as hard as you can and it gets you nowhere. The softer your opponent feels, the more you think you can throw him over. But you are easy to evade because you are using mus-cle power—arm tension.

Pushing Softly

When your arm is tense, it cannot feel; it is like a stick of wood. A skillful Push Hands player will push with soft arms. The momentum emanates from the body and through the arms in a wave-like motion, much like a whip. Since the arms are relaxed, they can feel how the partner is evading the push and can alter their direction to remain aimed at the partner's center of gravity. The arms are like heat-seeking missles zeroing in on the exhaust of a jet, but in this case they zero in on the center of gravity.

It is said that the palms must be like eardrums as they push the partner's arm or body, listening for the partner's center. So the palms and arms must be relaxed in order to be sensitive enough to "hear" inside the partner. Most pushes are done with the palms, yet arms, elbows and even shoulders can be used. When the push is accomplished, the arms must be relaxed enough to allow the wave of momentum and internal energy to flow through them. Thus, the arms feel like hollow tubes, allowing these energies to pass through freely. Any excess tension in the arms or shoulders is like dirt clogging the tubes.

Internal energy is much more powerful than muscle power. Teachers often demonstrate how people can be thrown many feet by a relaxed push using little physical motion. Yet if the same teacher were to use muscle power to push a person, a great deal more energy would be expended with little result. This is another "illogical" lesson of Push Hands. The more muscle power you use, the weaker the result. Muscle tension impedes the flow of internal energy. While a certain minimum of tension must be used in movement and in holding up the body, any further tension interferes with the greater power of chi.

An effective push is one in which the arms act as springs. As partner #1 begins the push, the springs compress. As the push continues, #2 is thrown back in a springy manner. The springs do not do the pushing, they only form a cushion between the two bodies. It is the body momentum and chi which are actually the powers behind the push. You can hardly even call it a push. Does a whip itself strike at its target? A person generates a wave of momentum with the whip, and the energy passes through it. The whip is only a passive conduit of energy. It is the same with Push Hands. The body generates a wave of energy which flows through the arms. Since the arms are not stiff, they are hard to resist; they are like a tidal wave.

Lessons of Push Hands

At this point, let us take what we have learned about Push Hands and attempt to use it in our everyday lives. All of us try to deal with pushes in our daily lives. People or circumstances push us into corners or attempt to throw us off balance. We are faced with people attempting to control us or throw negative emotional energy our way. Push Hands trains you to deal with these problems. Week after week of Push Hands class trains your attention and your body to react to situations automatically and in a way which leaves you in a powerful position.

When faced with a conflict, you know not to meet it head on. Never interfere with your partner's momentum (whether physical or emotional); let it flow by you or rechannel it. The fact that the other person is in an argumentative mood doesn't require that you match that mood. Many people enjoy arguments because they thrive on the energy they create. If the relationship of mind and Body-Mind within a person is based on conflict, he may perceive the world itself as based on conflict and be uncomfortable with calm. The world you perceive is a reflection of your inner state.

Whatever the reasons for a person's antagonistic behavior, it is perceived by the Push Hands player as energy and dealt with accordingly. You allow the other person to be as tense as he wishes while you yourself remain calm. An argumen-

tative person may insult you or make ignorant statements about a subject you
know more about. This is good fortune to a Push Hands player, for it means that
the other person has decided to entertain you.

"Look at all the tricks you are using to get me angry," you say silently. "I am
honored that you are spending so much energy to get me to interact with you.
You make your face look angry, you shout in a loud voice. You are pouring out
your energy to me. Thank you for giving me your energy."

You needn't get caught up in the energy pattern of another person. When the
other person finds he has nothing to push against and does not get his energy
back, he will give up.

Neutralizing Intimidation

The game of intimidation is surprisingly common in our society. It is really
a Push Hands game. There is an implied threat (the push), and your self-
confidence is thrown off balance. The boss, the parent, the teacher, the child,
the spouse can all try to get their way through the implied threat of firing, spank-
ing, withholding love, failing you, divorcing you or beating you. Even death is
a push. It is an implied threat in our society, just as failing is in school, and has
as much control over your behavior.

When you "do Push Hands" with these threats, you can neutralize their force.
Let's take the most extreme example—death. I will attempt to teach you to play
Push Hands with death and to learn to neutralize it. I will do this by giving you
a new perspective on life and death. When you were born, you were separated
from your source of life. First, you were separated from the placenta, then you
were kept separate from your mother for long periods of time, lying in your crib.
All primate babies need the constant touch of their mothers in order to grow up
without major emotional problems.

Then you are separated from the earth. Concrete lies beneath your feet, not
earth. Your food comes from markets, not directly from the earth. Your water
comes from the tap, not from a stream. Those living in cities are separated visual-
ly from the earth. All of us are faced daily with artificial geometric designs: square
rooms, circular clocks, rectangular windows and furniture, streets running in
straight lines, etc. Nature is random. The eyes need to see random scenery for
the emotions to be healthy. Concentrate on a bowl of popcorn and then on a
checkerboard and see how different you feel. Our attention is so separated from
BM that we don't even know how we feel.

Our schools teach little true history, only the history of conquest. What of
labor history? What of the history of the psychological evolution of the human
mind? What of the history of belief systems, the history of lifestyles of the average
person in various civilizations, etc.? Thus you are separated from true human
history. Ours is a life based on separation. You are taught that your body,
thoughts and feelings are "you," while your senses are "other." So you are also
separated from your senses.

There is another way. This way lies on the next mountain across a deep chasm. There is a bridge over that chasm called T'ai-chi-Ch'uan. Take that bridge. Now you are on the other side. There is no such thing as death opposed to life. All is alive.

If you were to eat a peanut-butter sandwich, would you call it alive? What about when it is in your mouth? Is it alive then? Is it alive when it is in your stomach? What about when it is in your bloodstream, your cells? Is it alive when its products are being excreted? When is the sandwich alive? "Life" is an arbitrary definition. That sandwich has the potential to turn into live functioning cells in your body. It came from wheat, peanuts and other "live" ingredients.

During the winter, plants are in a dormant state. They have the potential to grow next spring, but in their dormant state, are they alive? An acorn has the potential to become an oak tree. But is the seed alive? The earth in a garden has the potential to turn into the plants growing from it. Is the earth alive? We have learned from the science of ecology that the planet is one whole living system, just as an individual body is a living system. But in our training of separating ourselves from our environment, we have lost sight of this fact. Rather than being part of a living system, we experience ourselves as isolated objects peering out at other isolated objects, some of which are alive and some of which are dead.

Push Hands changes this. Each partner follows the other with great sensitivity, feeling within each other's bodies through the sense of energy. Eventually it is hard to tell where you leave off and the other person begins. It is experienced as a field of swirling energies, as if the nervous systems of two people have fused into one. The moment one of you attempts to isolate yourself through closing off your nervous system, you become insensitive and can be pushed over.

Rather than being opponents, you are truly partners helping each other open up to the environment. Once you have become open to another person, allowed your energy to flow together, you can do the same with your environment. Rather than identifying yourself as an isolated object, you identify with the whole flow of energy you experience.

In your Push Hands practice, you have learned that you have the greatest power when you do not interfere with these energies. Thus you must become very sensitive to the principles of nature, so that you may flow with them. You see spring follow winter. The land seems dead, then it springs to life. You see day follow night. Your body needs a period of rest each day as plants need a period of dormancy each year. The T'ai-chi student begins to understand the role of cycles in nature. The biological feelings of your connection to the environment become stronger than your feeling of isolation.

And what is this feeling of isolation? It is the feeling of "I am me as opposed to you." It is the feeling of resistance against change, of maintaining a rigid identity. Such a rigid identity is perceived as power because it links you to your society. You are a worker at a certain job, you have a certain type of personality, certain beliefs, you support a certain political party, etc. Being a member of a large city-state requires being molded into a certain role. This role, the societal identity, is perceived as the connection you have to the source of your needs, which comes from the structure of the society. This identity is a falsehood maintained through various rules invented by that society.

But when you begin to identify with nature, you realize an amazing fact—a fact which is the opposite from the teachings of many organized religions associated with city-states. The body is immortal; the identity is not. Atoms never die. Your body may physically decompose after "death" but it simply turns into worms, bacteria, plants and new animals. All that dies is that which is stiff. A stiff branch will break. A rigid identity cannot remain rigid forever. We can tell all the stories we wish about ourselves and famous people of the past. All our friends can agree with these stories. They may be told over and over again and remain unchanged if they are recorded well. But living systems do change. They are in a state of dynamic equilibrium—balanced change.

So as day turns into night, a physical body will die, rot and be transformed into other forms of life. Even whole species and whole solar systems eventually die. Yet life itself, the pattern of growth and change, continues. If you can become sensitive to the basic principles of nature instead of the stiff personal ego identity, you will become comfortable with this cyclic process of change and not think of it in a negative way. Life itself is immortal, though we, in our advanced civilization, continually try to destroy it.

By identifying with biological life, you become immortal. Your identity becomes more than just your body, if becomes the planet, the process of cyclic life, the whole community of living creatures. You will look upon the death of your body as you now look at the death of a cell within your body. A cell may die, but the larger being continues to live. Does this mean you will not "die"? No. You will decay just as everyone else does. Yet something very fundmental has changed within you. A dropping of resistance. Death is no longer a threat; its force has been neutralized.

Death is night, it is winter, it is the ebb of the tides. You die and a baby is born. A new story is made up for this baby. It is not your story. But perhaps the baby contains some of your molecules. Who knows which people in history have contributed their molecules to you? Much of your food is fertilized with artificial fertilizer made from oil which comes from prehistoric plants and animals. Most likely you have dinosaur molecules inside you. There is a pattern within you which takes these molecules and from them forms a life. This energy pattern is you—your body structure, emotional structure, psychological structure and thought structure. In your feelings of separation, you pit these structures against those of others to show how unique, how separate you are.

Push Hands blows this game. It connects you with the force of life itself, Tao, to show you your true immortal identity. It is not to maintain your rigid story that the world exists, but to continue the flow of life. As a part of life, you will never die—only change.

Opening the Field of Sensitivity

At first, Push Hands partners will compete with each other as true opponents. The important issue will be who pushes whom over most. Each will accuse the other of doing something wrong. Egos will be aroused. A constant watchfulness by the teacher is necessary at this time, in order to diffuse this competition. To get students to open up is a very difficult thing to do. It requires teaching them to let go of their emotional armor and become vulnerable.

One of the ways this is accomplished is by focusing the students' attention on the intricacies of the flow of momentum. Many little pulses of momentum are traveling between the players at any one time, each going in a different direction and containing a different amount of force. Any one of these pulses can be expanded by one of the players into a pulse of great force, throwing the partner over. This feels as if there were a long balloon between the two students. All of a sudden, a large bubble is blown on one end of the balloon by one partner, throwing the other over. Since there are many of these pulses or flows of momentum, both players must pay attention to all of them. If there is one either partner is not aware of, it will be "expanded" by one partner and the other will not be able to neutralize it.

When it comes to concentrating on the pulses, you cannot say whether the pulse is inside one partner or the other at any one time. These pulses are really created by the relationship of balances and movements between the two people. To the players, the "field" upon which Push Hands is played is created by the elimination of the barrier between them. If the partners are as tense and resisting as a rock, then the game cannot take place. It is the sensitivity and openness of the partners which creates the field of play. Unless energy is allowed to flow freely between the two players, Push Hands turns into just a shoving contest. The more the players' attention is focused on this field of play, the more the barriers drop.

After a push, the teacher might ask you to recall what happened, to remember the pathways of all the pulses leading up to the push. Thus the conscious, thinking mind is made aware of the principles of Push Hands, and is attuned to those principles. This develops harmony of mind and body. The field of pulses is really BM, for the pulses are created out of relationships of balances, the territory of BM.

Pushing and Shoving

You can easily see how Push Hands is effective training for making love, which involves the removal of barriers between people. Sex is no place for the performance of mechanical techniques. It requires a giving in to the flow of energies, a giving up of the feeling of isolation. Sex should not be something one "does" to someone else, but should be a form of "not doing" in which two BMs unite and play spontaneously in the "field" of energy. Only then can the total intensity of the sexual experience be felt. In your first attempts at sex, you want to do everything "right" to impress the other person. Sex is all too often just another form of trial or competition, as is the relationship of which it is a part. This shows an absence of sensitivity and openness. The two BMs are not involved in the relationship or in the sex, and thus the feelings of connection are not deep. This is how destructive the misuse of the mind can be.

The uniting of BMs is experienced as dropping the societal identity and identifying with the entire field of energies of both partners. In Push Hands, when you push your partner, you breathe in, breathing your partner into yourself in a similar manner as "breathing from the earth." The mechanics of breathing in your partner are as follows:

1. The pusher's arms are partially relaxed and act as shock absorbers or springs. As you push, you experience a two-way channeling of energy, as described in the previous chapter.

2. One wave of energy shoots up from your feet, through the Tan-tien and into your partner. The other wave shoots from your partner down through you and into the ground.

3. As you breathe in and push, you are feeling these waves of energy passing through your body. This gives you the impression that you have breathed in the energy of your partner. You must be open, with no blockages, to allow this energy to pass through your body. In this openness is a feeling of vulnerability. Since you are open, that is, relaxed and not resisting, you feel as though your partner could turn the tables and push you. Yet what is there to push? If your body is truly relaxed, your partner has nothing to push against. Openness does not make you vulnerable as long as you can let your partner's energy pass right through you. In fact, unless you are soft and yielding, you cannot flow in past your partner's tensions.

This teaches you that only when you are open and vulnerable do you have power. When you are closed to the energies around you, you are weak. The same is true in a relationship. How can a relationship work if both people are closed and unwilling to share their feelings? To remain open to energy and yet learn how to neutralize a push (an intimidation) is the skill developed by Push Hands, a skill leading to harmonious relationships.

To be able to flow through the resistance of a lover and share your love is another result of Push Hands practice. Imagine two people in love, both of whom are very sensitive to the flow of energy within their own bodies and that of others. Both have linked their energy patterns to the energy pattern of the planet so that the energy of the environment is flowing through them. In addition, through T'ai-chi-Ch'uan, they have learned to magnify their own internal energy and eliminate any blockages to it within their bodies. When these two people open themselves up to each other, their everyday feelings can be as intense as orgasm.

It is extremely important to be careful about who you open up to, for people with negative energy, those with a lot of emotional problems, can affect you intensely in a negative way. This is so even though they might not be doing T'ai-chi and you are the only one with that degree of sensitivity. Unless you are truly a "pane of glass" to their energies (which is very difficult), it is easy for your energy pattern to absorb and take on aspects of theirs. Then it will take a lot of work to rid yourself of these disturbances to your pattern. Similarly, it is important to choose who you do Push Hands with. If you practice often with a negative person, you will find yourself suffering.

For two lovers happily devoid of such a problem, the experience of love involves not only them; it feels as if the entire planet is participating in the love between them. In the chapter on healing, this will be explained in more detail.

Spontaneity

Neutralizing the intimidation of death and enhancing the experience of love; what else is the exercise of Push Hands capable of? It has the ability to bring BM out into the open. That is, BM is so strengthened by Push Hands that it becomes the predominate factor in a person's behavior. The implications of this change in a T'ai-chi student are enormous. BM does not take time to think and plan. It is spontaneous, connected to a source of knowledge much vaster than that to which mind is connected; BM is connected to the entire earth.

Living your life from mind is like a rat trying to go through a maze. It must investigate every pathway because it has no way of knowing which pathway leads to food. With BM, you can look down on the maze from above and at one glance see all the pathways and know which way to go.

T'ai-chi students are often amazed at the coincidences which start to happen in their lives. As soon as they need something, it just seems to appear. This is no "coincidence" in the normal sense of the word. It is not an accident. Push Hands teaches you to be sensitive to subtle happenings and to deal with them automatically, so as to maintain them in a powerful position. In this case, you are dealing with flows of momentum and chi, but in the everyday world, Push Hands training causes you to behave in the same manner. Yet, since it is being done automatically by BM, you are not usually aware of all the little manipulations of BM altering the relationship of internal and external energies in your favor and altering your reactions to innumerable everyday circumstances for your benefit. Therefore, when you finally realize that the circumstances are in your favor, it seems like a coincidence. Imagine the inner peace of realizing that there is an internal mechanism working to your advantage, constantly bringing opportunities within your reach, automatically helping you avoid harmful experiences. Once you have confidence that your innermost feelings and instincts are positive and beneficial, you can be spontaneous, because you trust your feelings. The everyday practical benefits of T'ai-chi practice give you the confidence to trust your feelings. Once you are spontaneous and don't have to calculate every move with your mind and guard your feelings so closely, you can be free and happy. You realize that *you* have been the guard who has locked your own happiness away, who has kept your power under lock and key. That guard is self-consciousness (as opposed to true self-awareness). As for lovers, when living from spontaneity and feeling, they can *feel* the needs of each other. A simple hug can do more than all the intellectual discussion in the world.

When you are discussing a topic, do you actually listen to others or do you just rehearse what you will say next? Are you interested in learning or only in being "right"? When you anticipate a meeting with someone, do you rehearse what you will do, or do you trust yourself to act effectively? The more you rehearse, the more you are saying to yourself, "I don't trust me. I have to plan everything out so I won't slip up."

To be fully effective in living your life, you must trust yourself. This gives you power. Perhaps when you were a child your parents jinxed you. "Don't spill that milk! You'll fall and hurt yourself! Don't fall off your bike!" While meaning to protect you, they actually broke your self-confidence. This is the meaning of spell-casting in the sense of witchcraft. By breaking people's self-confidence and implanting the seed of an idea in their minds, you can control their behavior. By controlling their behavior, you can affect their health and even their relationships with other people. This form of interpersonal manipulation, spell-casting, is commonly done by people who would never think of themselves as witches.

A well-grounded trust in yourself is essential in living an effective and happy life. There is a very good reason to trust yourself. There is a BM within you which is connected to the entire planet. You are backed by powerful forces. When you trust your BM, you are inviting it into your life. And then you become powerful—no more wobbling.

Body-Mind Loves to Play

How does Push Hands accomplish this? Push Hands is a game which the mind cannot play. Only BM can be aware of all those little pulses of momentum and keep the body in balance. As your studies progress, you become sensitive enough to feel the appropriate moment to push, when your partner is off balance, insensitive to a pulse of momentum or resisting such a pulse. Yet your mind is not fast enough to react at those moments, for they only last a second or less. It is only when the mind is dropped and BM takes over that you become fast enough. But since it is BM which is reacting and causing the push, you feel as if you yourself didn't do it, for you still identify with mind. Somehow the push happened, but you can't understand how. More and more of the Push Hands game is done by BM until it becomes totally a BM game. Once you have accepted this spontaneous and very effective entity within you as being a part of you, BM and mind can both operate at the same time.

While doing Push Hands, the partners can engage in an intellectual conversation and even joke around. The BM's are, meanwhile, conversing in their nonverbal way and also joking around. There are Push Hands jokes just as there are intellectual jokes, although they can't be translated into words. This is why there is much laughter in Push Hands and in T'ai-chi in general. BM loves to play and be happy. If there is no laughter in a Push Hands class, I question the quality of the Push Hands being taught. BM even loves to play jokes on the mind. You may often be surprised by your own Push Hands, for your BM will do some crazy little thing when you're not looking.

Haven't you ever made a pun and not realized it? But the way you phrased it was not how you would normally speak, so some part of you purposefully made that pun. This is BM. This is why you don't have to rehearse what you will say in social situations. As long as you're in touch with BM, the center of creativity, you'll never be at a loss for the right words.

Gradually you become more confident in BM's power and wisdom. You're not alone in the world anymore. BM and the entire earth is behind you. How can you be intimidated? How can you be sad? BM is the healer and that which knows of immortality. The mind knows it is mortal and that immortality is merely a legend. But when BM first sneaks onto the scene, taps you on the shoulder and says, "Here I am," the mind realizes that here is something more powerful than itself which is indeed immortal.

The BM is truly experienced as something tapping you on the shoulder. It is a real presence—a being as complex as you are—and far more powerful. The more you get to know this being, the more you realize how vast and complex it truly is. There is much more to you than the thinking mind. You come to realize that "you" (the pattern of thoughts, beliefs and behavior which is your identity) are a fiction, a tool, a creation of BM. For BM is pure creativity, and creativity needs play. The self, the ego, the mind, is the play of BM. When you experience BM, you experience your actual, real self.

We do Push Hands to reveal this great fact to the student. With Push Hands, there's no getting around it. Only when you give up your resistances, when you allow BM to "do" the Push Hands, can you do it well. There's no faking it.

So Push Hands is a very frustrating game. In order to do it well, you must give up yourself as total ruler of your being. You have to want to do Push Hands very badly to be willing to let go of the self (that is, the programmed behavior pattern) and face the real thing.

Gradually the qualities of BM, this spontaneous, playful self, are incorporated into the personality of the student. Your outward behavior will begin to reflect the fact that BM has taken over. Your life is no longer a series of battles or problems. It is a field within which BM can play. BM provides the power, the wisdom, the creativity of life. Mind provides the facts.

As you gain skill in generating pulses of momentum, you can send them not only in straight lines but in swirls and spirals. A baseball pitcher has his curve balls and screw balls, and a Push Hands player gives the pushes "personality" in the same way.

The Double Cones

In order to develop such dexterous manipulation, you must first master another T'ai-chi tool: the perception of the double cones. Above ground, the various pulses of momentum create a complex pattern. As a Push Hands player, you perceive another such pattern occurring beneath your feet, in the earth. For each pulse above ground, there is a corresponding counterbalancing pulse below ground. It is a mirror image of the one above, i.e., moving in exactly the opposite direction. If the top pulse moves forward, the bottom pulse moves backward as a counterbalance. Again, I won't say it's "as if" this were happening; it is indeed happening. My perception of the double cones is as vivid, as convincing as that of physical objects. Without this perception, I would not be able to play Push Hands well. The two patterns meet at ground level, at the bottoms of the feet. From the feet, they emanate upward and outward as well as downward and outward, forming two cones with the points at the bottoms of the feet.

Your ability to perceive these counterbalancing double cones in vivid detail is one of the breakthroughs that make Push Hands an internal game. External Push Hands concerns itself mainly with the positions of the arms and body; internal Push Hands concerns itself with the awareness of energy flow.

When you have developed the lower cone, you can absorb the push of your partner not only into your legs but into the lower cone as well. This lower cone is actually the root and can absorb the force of pushes, reroute the force and return it through the body and arms back into your partner. It can change the "spin" or qualities of a push. If a push is spiraling one way, the push will be absorbed into the lower cone, spiraled another way and sent back. Neutralizing your partner's push by absorbing it into the lower cone, the root, is called "internal neutralization." The alteration of the direction of rotation of a circular or spiraling push and altering a straight push into a circular or spiraling one (or vice versa) is much of the fun of Push Hands. You know what you're sending to your partner but you never know what you'll get back. Remember that there are many of these interactions going on at the same time and you'll get an idea of the intricacy of the game. Two or three pulses received from your partner may be transformed into one return pulse, while other pulses received at the same time may come back one-for-one.

Yin/Yang

This could be a madhouse if it weren't for a basic principle on which Push Hands is based. As discussed previously, the basic Taoist principle is Yin/Yang. This principle can be explained on many levels. Cosmologically, Yin/Yang are the two creative forces emanating from the primordial, unnameable emptiness (Tao). These two forces produce all the individual "things" in our universe. In personality, aggressiveness is yang and passivity is yin. Everything in our world is said to have either yin or yang energy or a combination of both. Night, black, female, gentleness, are yin. Day, white, male, aggressiveness, are yang. Even foods can be divided in this way, depending upon their effect on the body. Yin/Yang is really a description of the cycles of nature, and Taoism is a way of living in harmony with those cycles.

In Push Hands, yin and yang are often thought of as relaxation/tension. You try not to meet your partner's force with your own, but to neutralize the tension. Thus, you come in (you are yang) on the yin side of your partner. With a yang partner (one who is more tense), you yield (you are yin). You are like water, flowing around the rocks in a stream. This is called Yin/Yang pushing.

There is another form of pushing which is done right through the tension of your partner. In this case, your partner's tension is absorbed into your root at the same time as you push him. This is also based on the Yin/Yang principle, in the sense that a cycle, or circle, of energy is involved. Energy flows from your partner through you and into your root while it also flows from you into your partner. This is called the "wave push," as it feels like a soft, powerful, irresistable wave of energy. Even when your partner is in the air, he still feels that wave of energy following him and increasing in strength.

Of course, there is rarely a push completely of one type or another. Even as the push is being executed, the pusher remains sensitive and adjusts the balance of the two types of pushes from second to second (or from microsecond to microsecond). Learning to rechannel your partner's push and use his own energy to throw him over is not only good training for self-defense but for healing as well. The advanced Push Hands player uses as little of his own energy as possible. When you are pushed, you turn that force into a circle, sending it back to the other side of your partner. You sense the pivotal point of your partner and know just where to return the push to throw him over.

But you yourself try to be a neutral conduit for your partner's energy. When you learn healing (usually taught while learning Push Hands), you will be acting as a channel for the energy of the planet, directing that energy in healing ways into the patient. This will be further explored in the chapter on healing.

To be passive and yet in control of powerful forces brings about a great change in your outlook on life. It develops a deep-seated security and calm, a basic trust in the world—the feeling that the world is a positive place and that its natural forces are rooting for you. You are more willing to take chances in life and keep plugging away until you succeed.

Another change in outlook is the recognition of those natural forces as the source of your well-being. Those who experience internal Push Hands become ecologists, at least to the extent of understanding the importance of ending our destruction of the natural environment.

Push Hands is a practical exercise to turn the beautiful Taoist philosophy into a practical way of living. To "flow with the cycles of nature" sounds very nice, but how do you do it? Very often I have seen people who are "into being spiritual"; to them, it is merely another intellectual topic of conversation. Perhaps they act in a certain way they consider spiritual. They may seem all sweetness and light, but nothing has really changed deep down inside. Their pain is still being repressed. They are still not their own persons and, rather than live creatively, play a role which is acceptable in their group. Nothing has been released; a new role has merely been acquired.

Being Exposed

When doing Push Hands, sweetness and light will not help you. You must give up tension, let go of trauma and programmed thought and learn to concentrate, center and root. Push Hands does not leave you anything to hide behind. You are truly exposed. Your entire internal emotional state is displayed in your movements. A large part of the exercise consists of weeding out extraneous movements caused by patterns of tension, as was done in the Form.

First, there is the habit of tensing up when being pushed; in other words, resisting force. Second, there is the habit of being dramatic—making exaggerated movements. As your hand moves, touching your partner's shoulder, it may stiffen up, as if to say, "I'm planning to push your shoulder." In this case, your thoughts, your intentions, are being displayed in the movement. When your partner feels the stiffness of your hand, he knows what's coming.

This tendency of the body parts, especially the hands, to announce their intentions is called "telegraphing" and is a result of the mind controlling the body. Just as you try to give up control to the partner in order to gain power, you try to have your mind give up its control of the body so that the entire organism may gain power. Learning Push Hands helps your mind relinquish its control because you learn how beneficial it is to do so.

Only when BM is doing Push Hands and no telegraphing is taking place can you make your intentions invisible to your partner. BM doesn't plan its intentions in advance and then feel obligated to carry them out even if the situation changes. BM is not dogmatic; it sizes up the situation second by second; it is "present-oriented" and trusts its skill to come through at each moment. The emphasis is on sensitivity and spontaneity.

The teacher can tell what lessons you need to learn by the way you do Push Hands. If you don't pay attention to the world around you or realy listen to other people, you will find it hard to "listen" to what is going on inside your partner.

If you are not centered in life, if your attention is scattered, you won't be able to coordinate all the flows of momentum going on within you. If you have emotional walls within you and don't allow others inside, you won't allow your partner to come in very far during Push Hands. Before you have neutralized your partner's push by shifting his weight onto his back foot, he will already have begun to return the push, and this will cause you to fall off balance. If you concentrate on your looks and clothes and not on the qualities within you, you'll find it hard to work with the flows of momentum and will concentrate instead on external Push Hands (the positions of the hands and body).

A teacher can obtain a thorough understanding of a student's emotional makeup by watching these aspects of Push Hands. The goal is to allow you to mature emotionally by gaining skills in Push Hands. The teacher may even discuss the emotional implications of a particular quality or movement. As negative emotional habits drop, you are freed from their control. It is common to find students giving up cigarettes or coffee without consciously intending to do so. The emotional pressures causing these habits has been released and there is simply no desire to continue them. The greatest thrill of a teacher is to see the students change dramatically as they progress in T'ai-chi-Ch'uan. They gain confidence, alertness, health, calmness, creativity, enthusiasm, joy and warmth. They lose tension, anger, confusion, sickness and the feeling of helplessness. While I haven't heard of anyone becoming rich by teaching T'ai-chi-Ch'uan, it has its own rewards.

When two people first meet and discover that they both do Push Hands, one will say, "Wanna Push?" Doing Push Hands is a great way to get to know someone. To those watching it may just look like two people pushing each other around, but there is an intricate internal communication going on about states of consciousness. There is a sharing of the deepest feelings of energy flow with someone you've only just met, but Push Hands allows you to feel comfortable sharing deep feelings. Such relationships are usually very deep, sharing and caring.

Push Hands Exercises

There is another level on which Push Hands is played—as an exciting, skillful sport. In the beginning, you learn several "Forms" of Push Hands. these are mechanical, pre-set series of movements designed to introduce you to the principles of the game. After gaining skill in from six to ten of these Forms, you can go "free style," which means that anything goes. At the same time, you are taught several exercises introducing you to the dynamics of the game. Here are some of them:

1. *Falling Over*

The partners stand in the Push Hands stance, with front feet next to each other and about eight inches apart. You place your palms on your partner's arm, which covers his chest. Your weight is mostly on your back leg. Your partner's weight is mostly on his front leg.

   a. You push your partner very slowly, to the right, to the left, up and down and in various zig-zag patterns, until the partner falls over.

   b. Your partner's task is to drift away from your push like a balloon, floating in the air, offering no resistance.

   c. Each push should take about fifteen seconds from start to finish. Your partner should be flexible enough so that if you change the direction of your push as he is falling over, he can change the direction in which he drifts away, even though standing on only one foot at that point.

   d. Your art is to push in as complex a pattern as possible while constantly moving forward. Your partner's art is to follow the pattern and offer no resistance. At the very end, of course, your partner has to stop himself from falling by placing his front foot (which has drifted backward) on the floor behind him.

2. *Pushing Shoulders*

Two partners stand facing each other. Each one's feet are a shoulder-length apart and placed side by side (not at the corners of a rectangle or square).

a. Push the shoulders of your partner with varying degrees of force. The pushes should be quick and can be directed backward, forward or to the side. Each push should be done spontaneously; avoid a repetitive pattern of pushing.

b. Your partner should simply allow the upper body to respond to the push. This does not mean that he purposefully turns when pushed, but that the top of his body is so loose and devoid of mind that it will automatically turn with the push. Some people artificially turn their bodies when they see or feel you about to push them. This is cheating. You should make several false attempts to push, to trick your partner into artificially turning. Your partner can, of course, simply close his eyes so as not to see the push coming. Then you can touch your partner's shoulder without actually pushing, to trick his mind into turning the body. Only when the mind stops controlling the body will the artificiality be dropped.

c. When the body is loose and your partner's right shoulder is pushed backward, the body will turn clockwise. At the same time, the knees will bend, the left knee moving to the right to counterbalance the turning of the body. In this manner, the center of gravity is never thrown off.

d. When both shoulders are pushed backward at the same time, both knees bend forward as the top of the body bends backwards. In this case as well, the center of gravity remains in place.

e. If your partner is pushed sideways by placing your hand on the side of his shoulder and pushing, both knees bend in the opposite direction from the top of the body. Your partner's body should offer no resistance.

f. If you push your partner downward, however, (let's say on both shoulders at once), it should feel like pushing down on a spring—light on top but increasingly firm (never stiff) as you push further down. At a certain point, you won't have the strength to push down any further.

g. You can push downward and backward at the same time and use all kinds of combinations.

h. Another important point is that your partner should always return to the original position. He should imagine a rubber band attached to his chest and to the ground in front of him. As he is pushed, the rubber band becomes taut and pulls the body gently back into place.

i. The head must be kept in line with the body and not allowed to "hang" over frontwards as you are pushed. Try pushing your partner straight back (with your hand in the middle of his chest), first with his head hanging forward, then with the head in line with the body. You will feel the difference.

3. *Following the Hand*

Place your fingertips on the back of your partner's hand.

a. Move your fingers around, up, down, to this side and the other side. Your partner must follow all this with his hand and with eyes closed. It is his responsibility to maintain contact with your fingers.

b. Your partner's body must also move so that it is not the hand alone doing all the following. As your hand moves toward his body, he must turn and shift his weight so as to remove his body from the path of your pushing. Yet his body should remain as vertical as possible, with as little squirming and excess movement as possible.

4. *Stationary Pushing*

Assume a stationary stance, lining up your body in such a way that you are off balance in one direction only, your feet at the corners of a square.

a. Your partner, using only one or two fingers and extremely gentle pushes, must find that direction by feeling your body with his finger. He may push around the shoulder area very gently, until you fall over. In this way, your partner will learn that it doesn't take much energy to push someone over. The emphasis in Push Hands is on sensitivity—feeling balances within the partner's body.

5. *One Push at a Time*

This exercise is basically free-style Push Hands, but with one difference. Instead of having a continuity of motion, it consists of each partner pushing the other once and then stopping. It goes back and forth in this manner. If either of the partners gets pushed off balance, that particular push is repeated until the one who got pushed over finds the proper way to neutralize the push. This exercise is done as soon as the students begin free style. It gives them a moment between pushes to pay attention to what has just happened. It also allows them to experiment with different pushes and different neutralizations.

Hiding

Let me remind you of the basic idea of Push Hands. Each partner tries to push the other over and at the same time, neutralize the return push of the other. Each partner is using his palms to sense the other's center of balance and at the same time trying to be loose and yielding enough to hide his own center from the other. The feeling of Push Hands is like trying to find someone in a thick mist, but tyring not to let them find you.

There are many ways of hiding. As your partner pushes your arm toward your body, you can place the palm of your other hand on his arm, exert the same amount of pressure on the arm as he is exerting on yours and then withdraw your arm from the push. This is called "substitution." This maneuver must be executed very smoothly. If it is done correctly, your partner will not feel that anything has happened.

Another substitution can be used when your partner pushes your shoulder to the side. In this case, you can allow your upper arm (on the same side) to rise, substitute with your elbow and upper arm placed against his arm, then substitute with your other hand, withdrawing your first arm—a double substitution.

If your partner pushes forward right into your center with a straight, steady motion, this is a hard push to escape. You can try "splitting." As your partner pushes your arm, place your other palm on one of his arms, allow that arm to drift in a different direction and turn the body so that both of his arms pass by either side of your body. The most difficult aspect of Push Hands is that you are not allowed to force the momentum of your partner out of its natural path.

All of these maneuvers must be done by altering the relationship of balances of the two bodies and by "putting spins" on and slightly altering the direction of the flow of momentum. Your partner must think that he was the one who did it, not you. Each partner, therefore, tries to make the alterations in the flow of momentum as subtle as possible, so that the other doesn't notice it.

Push Hands is like sharpening two knives. You brush one knife against the other to hone them to a fine edge. Push Hands partners are honing their sensitivity so that they will be able to detect the most subtle flows of energy.

Tense Partners

Very often, you will meet someone who is not as subtle as he should be. Instead of springs, his arms may feel like two-by-fours. In such a case, you can't be totally soft, because your partner will simply grab your arms and twist you into a pretzel. This is true even of some T'ai-chi teachers I have met who spent many years studying Karate and then studied T'ai-chi-Ch'uan for only a few months and called themselves T'ai-chi masters.

With a tense partner, the tension must be "drawn out" and absorbed or grounded. At the first sign of such tension, you meet the partner's force with a spring-like firmness substantial enough to allow for only a slow movement towards your body. As the tense partner pushes toward you, gradually release the firmness of your arms as you absorb his pressure into your root and neutralize the push by turning, shifting the weight, etc.

One of my favorite maneuvers with such people is to allow them to build up pressure against my body to the point where they feel they are about to throw me over. Then, as they execute their push, I yield and turn, allowing them to push into the air, and they fall over. I may even help them a little by placing my arm around their shoulders and shoving them as I turn.

Feigning Vulnerability

"Drawing the partner in" or "leading him in" is an enjoyable part of Push Hands. As in the example above, you feign vulnerability to get your partner to do what you want him to do. The vulnerability in the example above was my faked inability to neutralize my partner's push. My favorite fake is to appear off balance. As my partner comes in for the push, I sink into the one foot I have on the ground and turn my body, adding a little shove to the partner as he falls over.

By playing with the limits of your balance, you will not only gain the confidence to take chances but will increase the fun of the game. By practicing how to deal with someone who takes advantage of your vulnerability, you will gain confidence in letting yourself be vulnerable and sensitive. This is because while the people around you may interpret your openness as vulnerability, *you* know that nobody can really "throw" you. The game of Push Hands allows you to be sensitive and open, yet powerful at the same time.

My Students Are Sane

There are hundreds of little lessons in life to be learned from this game. A student of mine surprised me a few days ago. For the first time, he skillfully used a lesson I had been teaching him for months. In the last chapter I discussed centering and the importance of pivotal points. One of those pivotal points in the body is the joints, such as the elbow. By putting a slight pressure on the partner's elbows just as he comes in for the push, you can neutralize the push. Even a slight tap will do it. My student's sudden skill with this method (and the degree of that skill) showed me that something had finally "clicked" inside him and had fallen into place.

That's the way it is in learning Push Hands. You become frustrated at your lack of progress month after month, and then, whammo, it clicks and you've got it. I compare it to defrosting a freezer. For hours, only little drips fall down, and then all of a sudden, a big chunk falls. But it took all those little drips to get the big chunk loose.

One thing that may have helped this student is that he practices juggling. Many T'ai-chi students study other forms of movement or spiritual discipline. T'ai-chi-Ch'uan either promotes curiosity and enthusiasm about the world or attracts those who already have it. In any case, it is rare to find a T'ai-chi student who doesn't have his hands in several other pies.

Another thing about T'ai-chi students is that for the most part, they are real characters ("strange" might be a good word for them). When visitors come to my school, I often try to reassure them that my students are really quite sane, only funloving.

Each school has a different character or quality. At the Long Island School we tend to be experimental and creative and avoid stodginess. I'm not interested in producing clones of myself or promoting some supposed "perfect way to be." I try to bring out the individuality and creativity of each student.

Many Fears

There are fears within many people which prevent their creativity and individuality from emerging. Push Hands is designed to replicate these fears on a physical level. It is a game of liberation of the spirit. The winner is not necessarily the one who pushes the partner over more times, but the one who is better able to let go of fear.

First of all, there is the fear of touching. As you may imagine, there is a lot of touching in Push Hands. Second, there is the fear of pushing another person. This is associated with the fear of hurting another person and of being aggressive. The Yin/Yang principle of T'ai-chi teaches you to develop a balance of passivity and aggressiveness. There is the fear of losing, of getting pushed. And there is the fear of letting someone into your own space, letting someone get close to you. There are fears of letting go (of relaxing), of getting hurt, of taking chances, of committing yourself (to a push), etc. The emotional significance of these fears is obvious.

It might take years of counseling to deal with such fears, but Push Hands takes care of them quickly, usually within several months. A rapport develops in a Push Hands class—a special kind of closeness among the students because of the dropping of these barriers between people.

Power from Sensitivity

In Push Hands we try not to interfere with the partner's momentum but only alter its direction or move out of the way. In this way, we are using the partner's strength against him and very little energy of our own.

Imagine you are playing Push Hands. You push into the center of your partner with your left hand. Your partner hooks his right arm under your underarm and presses your arm against his body. Your partner's left hand is pushing against the back of your left hand. At the same time, he spins his body to the right, sinks his weight into the back foot, then lets go of you. This spins you backward with considerable force, throwing you more than thirty feet.

What can we learn on an emotional level from such a maneuver? By remaining centered and using your strength rather than his own, your partner was able to throw you a considerable distance simply through sensitivity to the interplay of momentum. This sensitivity and understanding of interpersonal dynamics on a physical plane made him a very powerful person, although he may not have strong muscles. Power through sensitivity and awareness is the lesson learned.

Push Hands Imagery

A description of the game of Push Hands would not be complete without discussing the subject of imagery. And yet imagery is a difficult subject to understand without having experienced it. When you do the Form, you may imagine the qualities of the movements of a tiger and use those qualities as the basis of your own movements (as discussed in the last chapter). This is imagery: it is a way of linking your imagination with your physical movements.

The best way to describe the use of imagery in Push Hands is to describe what is known as "*The* Push". Students spend many hours just practicing how to push their partners, while the partners act as dummies, allowing themselves to be pushed. Besides learning to have springy arms, not using muscle power, zeroing in on the partner's center, allowing the chest to be loose and springy and pushing from the front leg, not the rear, the students learn imagery.

The pressure you experience as a pusher should feel like a mushroom, that is, very little pressure at first as the "springs" are compressed and then a constantly expanding pressure, as in a mushroom shape. Yet, this pressure must not come from stiffness, but from the movement and rooting of the body. (However, the muscles do have to be partially tense to create the springy pressure in the arms.) Any use of arm muscles to push as opposed to merely acting as cushiony springs, will alter the feeling/image of a mushroom. Students often find it hard to refrain from adding a little push at the end by stiffening their hands. In this case, the image of the mushroom will have a bump on top.

Another common mistake is to start soft and then, halfway through, harden up. In this case, the image is of a thin rectangle joined to a thick rectangle. (The soft beginning is the thin rectangle and the hard ending is the thick rectangle.) By using such imagery, you can assess your progress in working with momentum and energy in a "visible" way.

The entire Push Hands game is played with this imagery. One might hear a student describe a recent Push Hands "volley" like this:

"There was a black glob oozing through that area of white and as it oozed, it lost more and more of its substance until it was just a thin stream. But I still felt that there was enough left to touch me and that if it did, the stream would serve as a tunnel for more glob to ooze through to push me over. So I swirled the stream to the left so that it would run out of substance before you could reswirl it back toward me."

Anyone overhearing such a conversation might believe this student had developed a yin (soft) brain. Yet such visual imagery is a powerful tool in learning "*The* Push."

And when "*The* Push" is finally learned, it allows you to push a sizeable person a considerable distance with little effort.

Imagery has often been recorded by ancient cultures, resulting in mythology. There, the activities and adventures of heroes and gods were used as imagery. Once you understand the use of imagery as a teaching tool, these ancient writings make a lot more sense. There are many ancient teachings which, when understood, can vastly enrich our lives.

I am constantly amazed at how much there is to T'ai-chi-Ch'uan —how much of the universe it opens up for the student. It is meditation, health and counseling. It develops the imagination, coordination, interpersonal harmony and harmony between the individual and the environment. T'ai-chi-Ch'uan brings about inner peace, centering, calmness and joy. And yet, one of the most perplexing aspects of this art is the fighting aspect. How can we teach peacefulness and meditation and at the same time teach fighting? In the next chapter I hope to explain this apparent contradiction.

CHAPTER 4
KUNG-FU

One of the most confusing aspects of T'ai-chi-Ch'uan is that it is a system of meditation and yet involves fighting. From watching Karate movies, many people view Kung-Fu as barbaric, bloodthirsty and destructive. Certainly, many fighting schools are based on the concept of causing as many injuries to the opponent as quickly as possible. Students are encouraged to take out their anger on each other. The system of attaining color belts encourages competition but does little to develop individual maturity.

T'ai-chi-Ch'uan is quite unlike this. While the fighting is extremely effective (it was Bruce Lee's first style), it is actually a form of meditation and teaches many valuable lessons for personal development. The student must be completely calm and relaxed while fighting. Only in this state can his attention be sensitive enough to respond to his partner's movements. A calm mind means a relaxed body. Since T'ai-chi Kung-Fu uses internal energy, any tensions in the body act as a block to that energy. The body must be fluid and flexible, weaving in and out between the partner's punches and kicks.

There are no blocks as such. While the arms are kept close to the body to protect it, they do not move outward to meet the oncoming punch or kick. Such an outward movement would be a waste of energy. After all, if you have to move your arm out to meet a punch, that punch was not aimed directly at you anyway. You might as well just let the punch pass you by, while keeping your hands and arms in close to your body for protection.

Weaving in and out between the partner's punches and kicks requires extreme sensitivity and a fast reaction time. In fact, we try to get to the point where we know when the partner will punch before he knows it. In other words, we try to become more sensitive to our partner's behavior than he is. Only in this way can we drop the awkward, energy-and-time-consuming habit of blocking.

There is, however, something called "brushing aside" in T'ai-chi-Ch'uan. This involves making contact with the partner's incoming arm with your fingertips.

This is not done to turn aside his arm, but to sense his balance through his arm. In this way, you can direct your own punch more accurately into a selected target on the partner. T'ai-chi fighting is so fast that such a trick can give you a great advantage. There is simply no time to figure out mentally how to counter a move. It must all be done through sensitivity. There is also no time to first block and then punch. Brushing aside is done at the same time as your return punch, so that you are punching at the same time your partner is punching.

One of the beginning fighting exercises is to have one person initiate the punches and the second person only respond to the first person. Yet the second person's punch must land at the same time as the first person's. This requires an extreme reaction speed. Only with a loose body can this be accomplished.

Looseness has another benefit. When a loose body is punched, it yields. A tense body can be easily injured. A relaxed body will also allow the shock of the punch or kick to flow down to the ground and be dissipated there. When the body is tense, the shock wave remains in one place and causes injury.

Tenseness uses up energy. To fight for even fifteen minutes requires great stamina. If even a few muscles are tense beyond need, they can drain the fighter's stamina. In many fighting movies it seems as if the fighter's muscles are constantly tense. This is done to impress the theater audience and has no practical value.

Kung-Fu and Karate

As in every business, some things in some schools are done to impress the customers rather than to benefit them. I have talked to many supposed Kung-Fu schools which are actually Karate schools. When I ask what style of Kung-Fu they are teaching, they often reply, "We teach the best of all styles." This usually means that the teacher has seen lots of Kung-Fu movies but has little actual training. (There are over 400 Kung-Fu styles.)

It's common for Karate schools to claim they teach Kung-Fu, as the public is now familiar with the term and the interest in Kung-Fu is growing. This term refers to Chinese martial arts, while Karate refers to most of the martial arts of Japan. (Aikido and Judo are notable exceptions. They are not considered forms of Karate.)

In both Kung-Fu and Karate, there are hard (tension-oriented) styles and soft styles (based on the flow of chi). In my opinion, Kung-Fu is generally more chi-oriented and less tension-oriented. My conclusion is based on the many Karate people who have come to my school claiming that their style of Karate is based on internal energy. From what I have observed, their interpretation of "soft style" means just this side of a rock. Even the concept of letting go was difficult for them to understand. Whether these people truly represented Karate, I do not know. But for now, I do not view the supposed internal styles of Karate as having any similarity to T'ai-chi-Ch'uan.

In defense of Karate schools, they are giving the public what it wants. Many people simply want to learn to defend themselves in as short a time as possible and don't want to spend a year learning moving meditation first. Many people are just not interested in the meditation or health aspects of the martial arts and are strictly interested in fighting without having to give up their tension. The proliferation of Karate schools attests to the fact that indeed, *most* people are oriented this way. In addition, most people just don't have the time to get involved in a martial art with so many aspects to it. After work, rest and a social life, who can add another major activity to their schedule? There are also people who don't "believe in" meditation and personal development but do enjoy fighting. It's important to have martial arts schools catering to all types of interests.

In many of the Karate schools, the student is taught punching, kicking and blocking right from the first lesson. To me, this is going too far. In the old days, a student had to study for many years before learning fighting, waiting until his spirit was "ripe."

Attitude of the Student

There is the story of the swordsman who lived in the high mountains. A student found him and asked to study with him. The swordsman agreed on the condition that the student clean, cook and do the other work of the household. This the student did for a full year without receiving any instruction. In addition, he had to put up with the eccentricities of his teacher, who would sneak up behind him and hit him with a stick. After a year, the student knew just when the teacher was behind him and would counter the blow. The student was impatient and asked his teacher when the instruction would begin. The teacher told him that he was not yet ready. By the next year, the student knew when his teacher was entering the room with the intention of hitting him. But still, there was no sword-fighting instruction, only housekeeping. By the third year, the student knew when his teacher was even thinking of hitting him, and at that point the teacher said, "Now you are ready."

Nowadays things are quite different. I can tell the attitude of a new student by the questions he asks me. If he asks, "Can T'ai-chi beat Karate?" I suggest he forget about T'ai-chi because of his attitude. When people call me they generally tell me that they are looking for a martial art which emphasizes meditation, health and personal growth and that they have heard that T'ai-chi-Ch'uan offers a wholistic approach. This is the type of student I like to teach and one who will probably make an effective fighter.

When I studied T'ai-chi-Ch'uan from Grandmaster William Chen, I told him that I did not want to study fighting. He insisted that I take two months of fighting and then I could return to the Form and Push Hands. At the end of those two months, one of his advanced students backed me into a corner and started beating on me. I was shocked. What had I done to anger him? Out of the corner of my eye, I saw Master Chen watching and smiling. Was this a conspiracy? All I could do was punch as wildly as I could in hopes of getting out of the corner. The instructor backed off, not because I was such a formidable fighter, but because I was showing some initiative. At that point, something snapped inside of me. All the fear I had as a child of being attacked and pushed around vanished. I realized that T'ai-chi fighting was really an intensive way of washing away all the fear and negativity inside me. From that day on I enjoyed fighting. It has done more for me than a lifetime of therapy would have. I still believe that Master Chen told the student to give me a hard time, that he knew I was ready to have that realization and that I just needed to be pushed to experience it.

Because T'ai-chi-Ch'uan is a total evolution of the person and not just fighting, it takes longer to learn. When students ask me when they will be ready for fighting tournaments, I tell them in about five years.

"What if I practice an hour a day, every day?"

"Then ten years."

"What if I practice all day long, every day?"

"Then you'll never be ready."

I'm referring, of course, to the attitude of the student. You can't rush it. There's a natural evolution that takes a certain amount of time. If you force yourself, you'll miss your chance for this evolution to take place and you'll become un-balanced and warped.

Beginning Exercises

I begin the teaching of T'ai-chi Kung-Fu with several simple exercises designed to give students a feeling for the skills involved:

1. *Paper Game*

Each student has a strip of newspaper tied around his right wrist. With your right hand only, you must try to rip the newspaper from your partner's wrist. He must not use his left hand for blocking. It's a very simple exercise, but a very effective teaching tool. In a variation of the paper game, you must re-main stationary, not stepping (although you can move your body and hands). Several other players, who are allowed to step, try to rip your paper while you try to rip theirs.

2. *The Sandbag*

The sandbag is the workhorse of the class. At the beginning, you are taught to punch the bag without making it move. Yet you may not pull back your punches, as we never do that in T'ai-chi-Ch'uan. The punch must be forceful but loose, using the whole body, yet just reaching the bag at the end. You must stand far enough away from the bag so that the farthest extension of the punch just touches the bag. The elbow is never completely straightened, for this could cause injury. In a real-life fighting situation, a straight elbow is a tempting target for an opponent because it is easy to break.

In this way, you learn to judge distance, to reach far with the punch and to give up the satisfaction of taking your anger out on the bag. You also learn to control the force of your punch without pulling it back. If you train to pull your punch back, then when you are involved in a real fight it will be almost impossible to hit with a fully extended punch. Unless you can fully extend your punch without straightening your elbow, your fighting will be ineffective.

a. Bag as Partner. The swinging of the bag may be thought of as the movements of a partner. You are taught to duck and evade the bag as you spar with it. In this case, you must make full contact with the bag so that it will move.

b. Bag and Mirror. With the bag hanging in front of a mirror, you watch yourself in the mirror as you punch the bag, being careful to maintain correct posture at all times. You must pay no attention to the bag itself; it is the correct form of the punch which is important here. Aiming the punch must be done with peripheral vision.

3. *Rolled-Up Newspaper*

This is another stock-in-trade of martial arts. You hold two rolled-up newspapers in your hands. You thrust one toward your partner, who then must neutralize that paper and punch the other paper. The paper may be thrust at the student in various ways or swung in horizontal sweeps, as with a sword. In each case, the other student ducks or neutralizes that paper and hits the other. He can also then turn and strike the first paper as well.

4. *Beginning Glove Exercises*

You hold your gloves at the sides of your body and your partner strikes at them. After each pair of strikes, you move the position of your gloves. Your partner must continue striking, noticing the changing position of the gloves with his peripheral vision.

5. *Moving the Glove*

Your partner strikes at one of your gloves while you move the first. Without stopping, he must strike at the second glove, having kept its motion within his peripheral vision.

6. *Ducking and Striking*

To get used to the feeling of avoiding blocks, the following exercise is done:

a. You punch your partner in various ways, one punch at a time. Your partner ducks the punch as he punches you. Although he is reacting to your punch, both punches must land at the same time. Not only does he need a fast reaction time, he must also move into you in such a way as to avoid your punch, but without blocking you.

b. Meanwhile, you try to move your body in such a way as to feign a punch when you really don't intend one. This will cause your partner to strike unnecessarily; then you punch him for real. You trick him into moving inappropriately, so that you can turn the tables on him, ducking his inappropriate punch and punching him.

c. When this happens, your partner must be loose enough to reroute his own punch in midair and respond to your new punch. You can imagine the flexibility of body and attention involved in this.

7. *Frogs*

Let a tree frog rest on the top of your hand, keeping your hand still. When it jumps off, grab it in midair. Do this over soft ground in case you miss. While your grab must be rapid, it must also be soft, so as not to injure the frog. (Make sure to keep the frog's skin moist, as drying of the skin can be fatal to a frog.)

8. *Rubber Band*

Attach one end of a very thick rubber band to a hitting block (a panel of wood covered with a soft, shock-absorbing material). Tie the other end to a wooden dowel one-half inch thick and six inches long. Pull the rubber band taut, holding onto the dowel with one hand. Then let your arm loose, still holding onto the dowel. This will give you a feeling for the punch, as the rubber band pulls your hand into the hitting block. The T'ai-chi-Ch'uan punch is experienced as a release of energy, just as you are releasing the tension on the rubber band in this exercise.

9. *Catching Flies*

Catching flies in midair is a valuable fighting exercise. A classic Chinese movie shows a master catching a fly with his chopsticks. I once had to catch bats for some research work. This was especially hard to do (even in the confines of a large cage) because of the bats' sonar ability.

10. *Snake Strike*

Once I had a particularly vicious ten-foot python (non-poisonous). I would enter its cage and let it strike at me (it went for the face), ducking its strikes. This is an advanced exercise and should be done only with face protection and a partner standing by. I used neither, but that was in my younger and more daring days.

11. *Bullying*

Take a low stance, head low and arms and hands protecting your head. Your partner must punch you rapidly (about one or two strikes per second). You do not strike back, but neither do you move away. In fact, you move toward the striker, attempting to bully him by knocking into him. The striker must not back away either, but since you are knocking into him, he must move to the sides, like a matador, so he can continue to punch. You mustn't look up at the striker, but watch his feet, feel the strikes coming with your sense of energy and move your body and head so as to minimize the impact of the strikes.

12. *Hound and Hare*

We take a trip upstate (New York) to a particular area of forest I am fond of. Two people are the hounds and one is the hare (it can be played with more hounds). This exercise takes place at night. The hare is given a five-minute head start and then the hounds must find him. This exercise helps you develop sensitivity to another person's presence.

Here's an example of a hound-and-hare chase I was involved in. J. and I were the hounds, and K. was the hare. K. walked about two hundred feet down the trail and hid behind a bush in hopes of coming up behind us. J. went on ahead but I lagged behind, anticipating such a trick on the part of K. It was a moonless night. Sure enough, K. began walking behind J., but then both turned off down the mountain and I lost them.

The object of the game is to shine your flashlight on the hare, but if I had shined my light and K. wasn't directly in the beam, he would have been clued into my presence and escaped. So I had to be sure of where he was.

As I walked down the mountain, I felt a presence to my left and froze. I remained frozen for fifteen minutes, listening for some sign of K. While there was no sound, I was sure he was about a hundred feet to my left. Slowly, I brushed away the dead leaves in front of me with my toe, so that I could take a step without crunching the leaves. For a half-hour I continued stepping in this manner, until I was right over the place where I felt the presence. Still I could not see K., but the presence was so strong that I shined my light down onto the ground. K. had buried himself under a foot of dead leaves.

Mechanics of Fighting

The emphasis of T'ai-chi-Ch'uan is on awareness of energy, sensitivity and spontaneity. But still we must practice specific movements in fighting, just as we practice a Form with specific movements. These specific punches, kicks and evasions form a framework from which spontaneity and creativity can work. The punches and kicks strike like a whip with the whole body-weight behind them. A punch's power is a combination of shifting the weight forward, turning the body, a wave of momentum emanating from the earth through the fist, and the flow of internal energy. Each of these factors must be coordinated with the others so that they reinforce each other.

The body of a T'ai-chi fighter is often compared to a bow, with the arm as the arrow. The arrow has no power of its own; it's merely a messenger or carrier of the energy of the bow. It is the body which generates the power; the arm is a hollow conduit of that energy. Students must practice this style of punching by punching in slow-motion in the air until their posture and movements are correct down to the last detail.

Shoulders must be relaxed as well as the chest. Both knees are bent, and as the punch is executed, the rear foot relaxes and moves up just behind the front foot, with just its toe on the ground for balance. For the next punch, the weight is shifted to the ball of the rear foot for just a second, and then the front foot steps again. This leaves the feet loose so that the fighter may maneuver very rapidly between his partner's punches and kicks.

There are many types of punches to be practiced, from the spinning backhand punch to the reverse spiral double-jab and other such exotics. It is beyond the scope or intent of this book to list and describe each punch and kick. This is best left for an instructor to show you. It is the intent of this book to describe the principles upon which the fighting is based and how they apply practically to your life.

The punch, properly executed, should resemble a rubber band held in one hand, stretched back with the other hand and then released. In the same manner, the arm and the whole body must be springy to maximize power and speed. The momentum of an object is determined by multiplying its speed by its mass. The T'ai-chi punch has most of the body-weight behind it and the speed which comes from softness (relaxation of the muscles). You have a hundred pounds hitting you with great speed.

In addition to this, each punch is "depositing" your chi within the other person. This chi is not the same as momentum, for the force of momentum is felt at the moment of the punch's impact. Chi is felt one to several seconds later. It takes a moment for the packet of chi you deposited to explode within your partner's body.

This is the origin of the legend that a T'ai-chi fighter can send energy out of his palm to knock over his opponent without even touching him. I have never seen this "palm power" demonstrated, but I have experienced the mushrooming power of chi left inside me by a punch. The receiver of the punch tries to neutralize that energy before it explodes, but has only a second to do it.

The springy quality of the punch allows for rapid-fire punching, with each punch containing full force. I was once sparring with Master Chen when I first began learning. All of a sudden, the air was filled with punches. I thought several other people had joined in. All I could do was hide beneath my arms and fists. When the dust cleared, it was only Master Chen who had been punching me. Such machine-gun punching is often likened to a swarm of bees, buzzing around and stinging you. You can hardly defend yourself against such a swarm because it is insubstantial; there's nothing to punch against. T'ai-chi-Ch'uan punches are similar, as they are loose.

Loose arms are difficult to block. If your opponent blocks (assuming he is not a T'ai-chi fighter), your arm flows with the new momentum which has been added to it, spins around and hits the opponent anyway. Or your forearm may collapse from the block and the elbow will continue coming in; if the elbow is blocked, the shoulder will continue.

The Not-Doing of Fighting

Let's take a look inside a T'ai-chi fighter to see what he is actually experiencing as he punches. There is a pressure within him, waiting to be released. This pressure is chi. The trigger for the body to execute the punch and release the chi is the relationship of balance and posture between the two fighters. At just the right moment, the body spontaneously punches. The fighter who punched does not consciously understand how the punch took place, for he did not will himself to punch. He set up his own BM to execute the punch if certain conditions occurred. Then the fighter released himself to BM. His mind, his consciousness, just sat back and watched. This is the "not doing of fighting." It is instinctive. The punch is almost an afterthought, as his concentration is mainly on balance and awareness of energy.

The T'ai-chi fighter also ducks and evades instinctually. It is like trying to pick up a speck of dirt floating on top of a drink by using a spoon. The dirt just flows around the spoon, not because it has a mind, but just due to the nature of the forces involved. T'ai-chi Kung-Fu feels very similar. It feels as if it is just happening by itself.

In a real fight, you don't have time to figure out which countermove to use against your opponent's strike. Someone in the street will come at you wildly and not care how much he gets hurt. Unless your fighting is instinctual, you cannot deal with such a person. Highly stylized fighting is fine for movies but is ineffective against a street fighter. T'ai-chi fighting is really street fighting.

There is very little backing away. You duck toward your opponent, move in toward him and perhaps spin around behind him, but rarely do you move backward. The Form is actually composed of fighting movements and is designed to teach you how to deal with several opponents at once, such as might happen in the street.

Kicking

The kicks are also very loose; the weight of the body goes into each kick. To maintain balance, your body must sink in toward the leg which is on the ground. With side kicks, this is so much the case that your head and body sink below the horizontal and your head hangs upside down at the moment of the kick.

There are several exercises to loosen and strengthen the legs:

1. *Slow Kicking*

Several kicks are executed consecutively in slow-motion. This develops an understanding of the balance involved and begins to strengthen the legs.

2. *Corners*

One leg is lifted first to one front corner and then to the other, dipping down but not touching the ground in between. These movements are repeated up to 25 times for each leg.

3. *Crescent Kicks*

Each leg is spun in a circle in front of the body, representing the crescent kicks, while the other leg is on the ground. Imagine a point at head level and about three feet in front of the body which the leg passes as it circles. Repeat 25 times with each leg.

4. *High Stepping*

Jump from one foot to the other. The foot which is raised each time must tap an object one to three feet above ground level (such as a hassock or stoop) and two feet in front of you. This is done 50 times.

5. *Side Leg Raises*

Hop from one foot to the other. This time, the other leg must be raised to the side at a 45- or 90-degree angle from the ground. The eyes must watch each leg as it is alternately raised, so that the head is moving from side to side. The foot should be horizontal to the ground, so that the outer edge of the foot is pointed away from you. Repeat 50 times.

6. *Balls*

A small plastic toy football is hung by a string from the ceiling. It is kicked much in the same way a sandbag would be. But in this case, the football bobs around a lot, requiring a lot more footwork.

7. *Sandbag*

The sandbag is the standard practice tool of kicking. With it, you can practice developing power.

8. *Uphill*

Practice kicking a basketball or soccer ball uphill. This will strengthen and loosen the feet.

9. *Rock Hopping*

An advanced exercise, which is not recommended without proper instruction, is rock hopping. We go to the area of forest mentioned previously. There is a steep stream cut into glacial rock with boulders strewn around and tree trunks fallen across the stream. The width of the stream varies from twenty to fifty feet.

At night, we "run the stream," which consists of shining our flashlights ahead of us and running downhill at full speed, glancing off the rocks with our feet. As we land on a rock, we must already have decided which one to jump to next, so that we can leap off with the proper force and angle. Since it is nighttime, we have only the rocks in the narrow range of the flashlight to choose from. At times, we land on a slanted rock and have to allow our feet to bend and conform to the angle of the rock. So far, there have been no accidents. But we try to be loose enough so that if we do fall, we can allow our bodies to conform to the rocks loosely and not get hurt. It takes years of training before you can try this exercise.

The body of a T'ai-chi fighter is much looser than that of any other style I have seen. We do not stand like a solid brick wall, as in some styles. The body seems to be made of a loose spring (like a Jack-in-the-box toy) and can bend and weave with ease. This makes the head and body a difficult target. At the same time, if makes it easy to sneak around and through your opponent's defenses.

Instinctual Sensitivity

As in Push Hands, one of the principles in fighting is to let your partner control you; this deprives him of power. Be the speck of dirt in the drink and spontaneously flow around his punches and kicks. This is called "not being there." To your partner you feel like a phantom. He sees you but he cannot hit you.

There are two contradictory principles which are the foundation of T'ai-chi Kung-Fu. The first is to place total concentration on what you are doing. Mind should be left home, so that not even a single thought will distract you. There should be total commitment to each movement, with your full energy behind it.

On the other hand, your attention must be so fluid that your body's reactions can change from second to second, depending on the situation at the moment.

In the middle of a punch, your partner may duck, so your punch must alter its direction in midstream without losing power. Even as your punch lands, you must maintain this sensitivity to change. You do not tense the fist, but allow the blow itself to cause the fist to contract. Punches usually land with the middle joints first and then collapse, so that the area of the fist, from the knuckles to the first joints of the fingers, are in contact with your partner. During that fraction of a second when the fist is collapsing, your body must align itself to allow the maximum flow of force into your partner. This alignment can double the effective force of the punch. The fist itself must remain so sensitive that it can sense your partner's balance and convey the proper information to your body, so it can align itself properly.

All this takes place in a fraction of a second and will give you an idea why T'ai-chi-Ch'uan is called an "internal style." It's not just a question of learning a certain number of kicks and punches and using them in the proper sequence. It is sensitivity training in the extreme. Two fighters may stand facing each other for a long time, hardly moving. Yet there's a great deal going on. Each is tuning into the energy pattern of the other, trying to catch him in an unguarded moment.

But this unguarded moment is not something one can discover by thinking. It is a feeling from the gut. And when you finally release that punch, you are as surprised as your partner. The two BMs are playing with each other, those natural creatures to whom the thousands of years of civilization are but a story. Your BM is back in the forest, facing a hungry tiger. Your instincts and your body are as fresh and alive as if you had grown up in the wild a million years ago. The two fighting partners are not interested in how many times they punch each other. They are going for bigger stakes—opening their consciousness to the power and awareness which animals in nature have always possessed but which we have repressed. They are fighting not a tiger who intends to eat them, but an internal programming which has robbed them of their natural power.

In an artificial civilization, our senses, our sensitivity, our entire being is out of place. For millions of years our bodies, emotions and minds have evolved to fit into a natural environment. While the external quality of life has improved, our awareness and sensitivity have deteriorated. There is no longer any need to keep our senses sharp to detect dangerous animals lurking behing trees. We often get little exercise. We hardly even walk anymore.

T'ai-chi-Ch'uan is a way of maintaining our natural health and alertness without returning to a more primitive way of life. Fighting restores your senses, reaction time, internal power, stamina, balance and coordination to their height. At the same time, it teaches you how to remain calm in a tense situation.

Social Benefits of Kung-Fu

Socially, Kung-Fu teaches you to let yourself be vulnerable to others, just as in fighting you are relaxed and duck toward the other person's punches. You learn to be spontaneous in social situations and not rehearse your every move, just as fighting is spontaneous and not technique-oriented. While committing your full energy to a project or relationship, you remain sensitive to alterations in the situation and are flexible enough to change with them. In this manner, one partner in a relationship never grows away from the other. This is similar to the punch: you use your full force for each punch, yet can change its direction in midair and even spiral around with the other hand before the first punch lands.

Fighting also helps you get over the anger and fear within you. You are placed in a situation which represents all the ways in which others have tried to force their will on you. Your anger has grown from earliest childhood because of these situations. Now, in class, someone is actually attacking you. At first, you try to strike back in a tense, angry way. Beginning students are the worst. All they want to do is kill, to knock your head off at the least.

When I first began to help instruct beginning fighting classes, Master Chen told me not to duck too often, so that the students could get the feeling of hitting me. I also could not hit them back too hard or they would get discouraged. During the summer, I used to go home with headaches. Gradually, the students learn to link up with the energy of their partners, which causes them to open up their feelings. This is a fearful time for them, as they feel vulnerable. But finally, the partner is no longer an opponent but part of a two-person energy-balancing system. The feeling of isolation, of me against him, drops and with it, the anger and the fear. Kung-Fu represents all battles, emotional and psychological as well as physical. By learning T'ai-chi Kung-Fu, you not only learn how to fight, you learn how to give up the internal battles you have been carrying around for years.

Another peculiar effect of T'ai-chi Kung-Fu practice is the expansion or dilation of time. After moving so rapidly and making such split-second changes in movement, when the T'ai-chi-Ch'uan student returns to everyday life, everything seems to be taking place very slowly. Each second seems to be a long time. One of the reasons you can react more quickly to situations is that they seem to be taking longer to occur. Thus, you not only live longer due to increased health; your subjective lifetime increases as well. The elixir of life is not some potion in a cup, but the teaching of subjective time expansion, one of the results of T'ai-chi-Ch'uan.

Punching into the Future

Within Kung-Fu, as within the Form and Push Hands, are many lessons of life, some of which have been discussed above. The punch represents the ability to change your circumstances in life, the power to influence your future; it is really a magical model of personal power.

To a fighter, the punch feels like a release of energy. You use that internal "rubber band" feeling. One end is placed on that spot on the partner who will receive the punch and the other is "held" by you, the puncher. In the second step, you increase the tension on the rubber band and in the third, release that tension, your fist flying into the proper spot like a released rubber band.

When you want to change your future, you can use these same three steps. First, you "attach" one end of the rubber band to the future. This means that you must imagine the circumstances you wish to occur very vividly, so vividly that they seem real to you. You must be able to "taste them."

Next, you increase the tension on the rubber band by living your daily life as if you are sure that the circumstances are going to happen. You must prepare for them; in fact, you must live your life as if they were already real. Get rid of the "as if" feeling and live your dream.

The last step is to let go of holding your end of the rubber band and allow it to pull you into the future. This means that you must allow yourself and your present circumstances to change. This is a process of letting go, not of a rubber band, but of beliefs, habits, even people and activities. It is an examination of what has to be sacrificed to achieve the future you desire.

Magical Fighting

This manner of relating each activity in T'ai-chi to gaining more influence over your life is called T'ai-chi or Taoist magic. Here, the word "magic" refers to methods of developing the personal power to improve your life. It is the central theme of this book.

Let's continue studying the punch. The fist forms on its way in, the hands being open and relaxed at all other times. the moment after the punch, they open up again as the arm springs back. To hold the fists constantly closed would be a waste of energy and a block to the flow of energy. The fighter never actually clenches his fist; it is the pressure of his loose fist against the partner's body which tightens it.

What does this teach us? The clenched fist may be likened to a pattern in our minds, an attitude such as anger towards someone. If we hold our fists constantly closed, this will harm us. If we hold anger within us, it eats away at us, while it may have no effect on the person against whom we bear the grudge. Yet, at the moment someone does something against us, it is quite natural, even emotionally healthy, to get angry. By punching in the manner described above, we learn to use our power and energy only at the moments when it is necessary or appropriate and to relax that energy at all other times. In this way, we increase our efficiency.

Perhaps this may seem cold: some people might argue that they can't help being angry all the time; it's just part of human nature. I don't believe that being a slave to anger and self-pity is truly part of human nature. I have a higher regard for it than that. These magical practices don't make you cold and emotionless. They simply allow you to drop self-destructive habit patterns so that you can become truly human. We can be as powerful and magnificent as a tiger or an antelope. In fact, I have yet to see a tiger do a human Form, but many humans do a tiger Form. We have many abilities tigers lack, such as extreme adaptability.

Another point in fighting is not to look into your partner's eyes or at his fists. Your attention should be on the upper chest area. This will give your peripheral vision a full view of his body. In your own life, you must learn what to focus your attention on. Often, if you concentrate on what you believe is the central issue, you'll miss all the peripheral action, which may be just as important. You fail to see the whole picture. By using holographic attention, as discussed in the chapter on the Form, you can become aware of all the various aspects of a situation at once in order to better size it up. This is especially important in conversation. By hopping from one point to another, a person can easily confuse you if you only concentrate on the immediate point being raised. You become dazzled by all his words. This is a method people often use to control others. But by maintaining your concentration on the central issue of the conversation, you can use your peripheral attention to listen to all the particular points. This way you'll never lose track of the central issue and become confused.

This is a difficult thing to do. There's a temptation in fighting to look at those gloves or those eyes. There's a temptation in conversing to exert your opinion on every issue being raised without regard to the basic subject of conversation. The ability to concentrate on the upper chest in fighting automatically helps you in your verbal interactions with people. The real magic is that simply by progressing in physical exercises, your personal life improves automatically, "by magic." This is not unnatural, mysterious magic; it is quite natural.

Fighting for Fun

Besides its psychological, physical and emotional benefits, T'ai-chi Kung-Fu is also an enjoyable game. Rather than the grim, angry faces you may see in a Karate movie, my students often smile as they fight. As in all games, this one has its tricks and maneuvers. One is to purposefully leave part of your body unprotected in order to encourage your partner to punch or kick. Of course, you must seem unaware of your vulnerability. When your partner strikes, the opening instantly vanishes and gives way to a return punch.

One of my classmates back in the old days used to let his hands hang by his sides and leave himself completely open. Yet it was very difficult to hit him. He was fast, and as soon as I came in for a punch, one of his hands swung around and connected with my head. The T'ai-chi-Ch'uan punch can come from anywhere. As you scratch your head or stand with your hands in your pockets, a hand will suddenly whip out and strike. It is therefore very difficult to tell when a T'ai-chi fighter will punch you.

There is a lot of feigning in sparring. Your partner may constantly pretend he is about to punch you in order to get you to overreact and open up your defenses. Thus, your reactions must be careful and not exaggerated. Then there is the old "Whoops, I missed" routine. You miss on purpose, step behind your partner and spin around with a backhand to the head followed immediately by another spin in the other direction (still with the weight on the same leg) and a backhand to the head with the other hand. The spinning motion of your body and arm creates a great deal of power.

In T'ai-chi Kung-Fu, we practice many styles or patterns of movement. You may build up the expectations of your partner by sticking to one style and then, all of a sudden, switch to a totally different style. This new style may last for only a few seconds, then you may switch to a third style, and so on. Your partner must be equally fluid in his behavior and not allow any particular pattern to trap him. Yet each partner tries to lock the other into a pattern.

It is easy to detect when your partner is locked into a pattern. His movements will not be linked to yours. His movements will be directed by his intentions, by his mind, and not by the actual relationship of balances and postures between your two bodies. Once he has lost this link to the intricacies of the situation at hand, it is easy to come right in with your strikes.

A T'ai-chi fighter does not prance about with fancy movements to impress his partner. His stance is quiet, his attitude calm and watchful. He is as linked into his partner as a cat is linked into the movements of a mouse nearby. Watch the cat. It does not prance about in front of the mouse to impress it, but remains still and watchful. Every cell of its body is tuned in to the movements of the mouse. The cat is a coiled spring of power. All of a sudden, that spring is released and the mouse is in the cat's jaws. Similarly, it is the simple punches and kicks which are most effective. Too often, students practice the fancy ones and neglect the simple ones. They find out to their dismay that most of the time they need to use the simpler moves.

Of course, once the foundation has been laid, it's fun to experiment with more exotic movements. Whenever a student comes up with a particularly strange, inane and generally ineffective move, the whole class will stop what they are doing and congratulate the student on entertaining them with his antics. Just as often, though, a student will come up with quite effective moves. These are not pre-planned, but emanate from his creative center, BM, and the student is as surprised by what he did as we are. All of us then practice this "teaching" which has sprung from his inner guru, BM.

Just as there are Push Hands "jokes," there are also fighting jokes. One of my classmates at Master Chen's studio loved to use spinning backhand punches. Unfortunately, he was not well rooted. It soon passed through the class grapevine that all you had to do was lean back and stick your foot out and this fellow would trip over it. This provided a lot of entertainment, and even he had fun trying to avoid tripping.

Besides acting like tigers, snakes and other creatures of the wild, students will sometimes attempt to imitate Groucho Marx, Charlie Chaplin and other such Kung-Fu experts. In one of the advanced classes, I have the students imitate each other. In this way they free themselves from rigid behavior patterns, develop more sensitivity to their classmates and diffuse competition. It is as if they are saying, "This is the way I see you," and one of the bases of competition is to make others think well of you. By turning this into a light-hearted game, the issue of self-image is diffused and students can open up more to each other. The subject of the imitation often exclaims, "Is that me?!" Thus you learn that the patterns of behavior others see are not your true identity; it is the fluid creativity within you that is your true self. This true self thrives on fun.

Laughter and Fear

If there is no laughter in a Kung-Fu school, then BM is not present. If you must bow to the teacher, call him by a stylized name and do twenty push-ups if you make a mistake, then in my opinion you will never learn the deeper aspects of Kung-Fu there. If the students tell you that he is the greatest Kung-Fu master in the world, then most likely you will learn very little of value from that school. A teacher must be a human being first, a Kung-Fu artist second. Kung-Fu is a joyful art, and the classes should be joyful.

What is it, then, that prevents some martial artists from releasing the joy within them? It is fear, the guard at the door of the dungeon holding BM captive. This fear may be expressed in many ways. You may be afraid of people, of closed spaces, of heights. But I think you will find that all of this fear can be related to the fear of allowing the inner being to escape.

For years, we have altered ourselves in every possible way in order to become acceptable to our peers. There is a fear in many of us of being ourselves—the innocent, playful child. In conversations, we must always be "right." In business, we must make more money. In martial arts, we must hit our partner more than he hits us. The fear of being the lesser person drives our behavior into destructive patterns: A martial-arts teacher must be the best and strongest teacher, able to beat up all his opponents. Only then will he have his share of students. The guru must be able to perform amazing feats. Only then will he have his disciples.

What should you look for in a Kung-Fu teacher? Hardly someone who has succumbed to this pattern of behavior, who hides behind a certain role so that his true self can remain locked up and his behavior be motivated by fear.

Turning fighting into a joyful game has the effect of neutralizing fear. If you can laugh while being attacked in class, how can fear have any power over you? If you remain calm, relaxed and joyful as you spar, how can anyone make you tense and anxious or intimidate you? You do not drop your fear *of* anything in particular. You learn to neutralize fear itself and deprive it of power. Even though you have learned to drop fear in the midst of protecting yourself from attack, the behavior of self-protection still remains. It is just that you are no longer paralyzed by fear. You have released yourself from your own prison.

CHAPTER 5
HEALING

It seems surprising that anyone would doubt the modern disease theory, knowing the apparent success of its application. Yet this chapter compares two disease theories, attempts to show how each theory is inseparable from its culture and how a better state of health can be maintained through the use of a combination of Eastern and Western disease theories.

The important question is, "Why do we get sick?" Each disease theory is based on a central idea or "organizing principle" (O.P.). This principle may be thought of as a particular aspect of the problem we choose to look at. Modern medicine is often accused of not being "wholistic," that is, it pays attention to only a few aspects of the patient and not his whole being. When one symptom is cured, another may take its place because the underlying cause of the disease has not been dealt with. Modern medicine is based on the O.P. of "matter," as opposed to "energy" in the East.

With the discovery of the world of microscopic organisms by the use of the microscope, the cause of disease was felt to have been discovered. Certain diseases are always associated with the presence of certain microbes. When a pure strain of disease-causing organisms is introduced into an animal, that animal is likely to come down with the corresponding illness. Further discoveries pointed to the excretion by these organisms of certain chemicals which are the mechanism by which the symptoms are caused. Disease, then, is likened to an invasion of a foreign army consisting of microbes. The army's weapons are chemicals. Due to the rapid breeding of these microbes once a certain number of them invade the body, it takes only a few days to create a full-sized army. The body engages in battle with the army. White blood cells engulf the soldiers and various antibody chemicals destroy them.

The function of medicine, it is thought, is to act as a friendly power, sending added armies to the body's aid to destroy the invaders. Diagnosing a microbial illness is easy. You take a sample of the blood, examine it under a microscope and watch for any microbes known to cause the symptoms of which the patient is complaining. Another technique is to culture a sample of the patient's blood, a swab of his throat, a swab of the genital area, or whatever area of the body is in question. The resultant colonies of microbes can be easily seen. Then a chemical generally known to kill that species of microbe is introduced into the body. It is a very simple, clearcut method.

The question still remains, however, why did that person get that illness? Why do only certain people get sick during an epidemic? The usual answer is that the others are "naturally immune," which is simply another way of saying that they didn't get sick, which explains nothing. Supposedly, these immune people had the proper chemical weapons at their disposal at the right time. You can see how this view of disease borrows its perspective from the military. "Fighting disease" is an imagery we've all been programmed with. We wait around until an enemy invades us and then go to our arms supplier for the proper weapons (which are available at exorbitant prices).

Even for diseases caused by malfunctioning bodily parts, little thought is given to why they malfunction. The emphasis is on repairing the malfunction rather than on a true understanding of the cause. We have a crisis-oriented medical system, concentrating on curative rather than preventative medicine. Many billions are spent on drugs and operations, but comparatively little on health education, exercise and a good diet. Yet medical science can hardly be faulted for its emphasis on curing rather than prevention. This is its specialty, and in this specialty it has developed miraculous techniques.

The Energy Perspective of Disease

We must look to a different perspective, a different O.P., to learn about the prevention of disease. This is why there has been such an upsurge of interest in T'ai-chi-Ch'uan, yoga, shamanism, natural diet and other health-maintaining systems. Even medical doctors are now studying these methods to develop a more wholistic medical system, and the future looks bright for a melding of these perspectives.

The above-mentioned health systems are based on an "energy" O.P. T'ai-chi describes the flow of internal energy along certain channels (meridians). If these channels are blocked, there is an energy buildup much like the buildup of water behind a dam. This buildup can cause discomfort in the short run and damage in the long run. In addition, energy can be concentrated in certain areas of the body for long periods of time, depriving other areas of energy. Constant thinking or permanent tension can create a rigid pattern of energy, concentrated in the brain or in certain muscles and nerves.

A balance of energy flow is essential for good health, according to the energy O.P. Should a large amount of energy be required to eliminate a particular species of microbe, for example, the body would be hindered if most of its energy were tied up in thinking or tension. The constant use of the brain or tension of muscles will weaken them unless they have time to rest.

A healthy state is one in which there is a basically even distribution of energy throughout the body. There is also an absence of blockages to the flow of energy. In this way, energy can flow to certain areas when needed and then return to the original, evenly-distributed state as soon as the need is over.

Harmonizing with the Planetary Energy

This energy is part of the energy system of the planet. Just as a plant absorbs water and nutrients through its roots, humans absorb energy through the earth. Just as plants absorb sunlight from the "sky," humans absorb energy from above as well. There is a constant flow of these two energies which I call "earth-air energies." So not only must the body be free of energy blockages within itself, it must also be free of any blockages to energy between the body and the environment.

Through the practice of T'ai-chi-Ch'uan, we gradually dissolve such blockages; only then do we actually experience the energy. It is as if we have been breathing through a narrow straw all our lives, getting very little oxygen, and then all of a sudden, we are allowed to take a full breath. Similarly, the experience of the full force of the earth-air energy makes us realize how deprived we have been.

Just as there is a world of microorganisms which was discovered comparatively recently, there is a world of living energy of which medical science has barely a hint. The limitation of our senses deprived us of the knowledge of the microscopic world for a long time. An instrument had to be developed to enable us to see such small creatures. But the world of living energy can be and is perceived by those trained to do so. And those people have noticed, over thousands of years, that the presence or absence of certain qualities of energy has an effect on us, much as the presence or absence of nutrients affects us. This is easy to understand when we realize that such energies or vibrations as sound (music) and light (specific colors or scenes) have an affect on our emotions. We tend to interpret this to suggest that it is the psychological meaning of the music or scene that affects us. But what is the meaning of music?

There are many such energies, some of which we are not familiar with, which affect us every minute. One of the jobs of a system such as T'ai-chi-Ch'uan is to develop the student's sense of energy and give him the skill to work with those energies to enhance his life and stay healthy. This practice is called "Chi-Gung," the teaching of perceiving and affecting energy. The work of a student is to keep his chi (internal energy) in balance within his body and in balance with the environment.

For example, there is a change in the quality of energy when the seasons change. At such times, the student must adjust his own pattern of energy to maintain harmony with the changing energy around him. At the Long Island School of T'ai-chi-Ch'uan, we hold festivals at the beginning of each season, inviting the public to participate in workshops which harmonize the individual chi with that of the planet.

Another change in the the earth's energy takes place when natural areas are destroyed or polluted. Covering the earth with concrete, for example, has a negative effect on the energy. The presence of trees and flowers has a positive effect. This is easy to understand for those involved in electronics. If there are two pieces of sensitive electronic machinery in very close proximity, one may interfere with the other. In a similar way, restructuring the physical environment has an effect on the energy in that area that can be detrimental to our health. Japanese rock gardens are planned precisely, not only for the visual effect, but also for the flow of energy among the rocks. They are very peaceful to be around.

House Medicine

We usually do not take energy flow into consideration when decorating our houses. Even the word "decorating" implies visual beauty. Setting up your house for its effect on your feelings is part of preventative medicine from an energy O.P. You spend a great deal of time in your home, so its effect on you is very influential to your health. "Decorating" your home from an energy perspective is a good way to begin improving your well-being.

The several principles described below will help you use your home as a form of preventative medicine.

1. *Sacredness*

Sacredness has a lot to do with caring. If you are in love, you care about your partner; he or she is very special to you. When you think of your partner, you experience a rush of good feelings, a rush of energy. Your immediate surroundings seem brighter and more pleasant. You could say that your partner is sacred to you. In a similar way, a sacred attitude toward the other aspects of your life is essential in maintaining health and good feelings.

Look around you now if you are in your home. Can you say that you have a sacred feeling toward your home? When you meet your lover, you pour out your love in the form of kisses, hugs and fond looks. I'm not suggesting that you kiss and hug your home when you enter it, but that you show your respect for your home. When religious Jews enter or leave their homes, they kiss the *mezuza*, a tiny box containing passages from the Bible which is secured to the doorframe. The Bible is a representation of their way of life, the principles by which they live. The particular passages in question tell them to love and obey God. The *mezuza* ritual is a reminder of their dedication to those principles in their everyday lives.

American Indians "smudge" themselves each morning after getting up and each evening before going to sleep. Smudging consists of lighting a container (often a seashell) of sage or other dried plants and wafting the smoke over their bodies. This ceremony is a symbol of their dedication to their way of life.

In each case, it is really their lives which are shown to be sacred. It is a way of uniting the profane with the sacred, of making their ordinary, everyday lives seem special and important. The participants in these ceremonies are saying that they care about their lives, the principles by which they are lived and even about their dwellings.

This adds a whole new dimension to life. It fills you with purpose and therefore with power and energy. Your home is not merely a nicely decorated box, but a window to another dimension, the living stage upon which your growth as a mature human being takes place. The door to your home is a doorway to power and wonder. Isn't this why we visit our churches, synagogues and temples? They seem to be holy places where unknown powers commune with us. Why should we have to visit a church to feel this? Our own home, humble as it may be, should be as holy, as inviting to those unknown powers as the finest temple. Turn your home into a temple. No drug will prove as effective in maintaining your health as living in a place you feel is sacred. Those unknown powers you will be communing with are your own internal energy and the energy of the planet. Your own home will become the meeting ground of those powers. It will be the biggest and most powerful pill that has ever been developed to cure disease.

The ceremony which is used in T'ai-chi-Ch'uan to enable you to feel sacred is the Form. These beautiful movements are often done right after you wake up and just before you go to bed. I try to do the Form in the back yard just after sunrise and just before sunset. This sets the pace for the entire day. It not only makes the house feel sacred, it makes the day feel sacred as well.

Perhaps you wish to create a ceremony for yourself. Think of your way of life, of the principles you believe in. Try to represent these in your ceremony. Putting a new flower in a vase each morning can be a ceremony. Lighting a stick of incense, reading passages from a book and lighting candles can all be ceremonies denoting your feeling of sacredness about your home and your life. When you have developed this feeling, the petty irritations that affect us can no longer have power over you. You live in a place of power, an abode of the Gods; how can you stain such a place with pettiness? When petty feelings cease to drain your energies, you are less susceptible to disease.

Another strange thing happens when your home becomes sacred to you. When you invite people to your home, you become aware of the effects of their energies on your home. You will tend to invite only people with positive energies. Your friendships thus become more selective. Other people will notice the change in the atmosphere of your home and the change in you. Those who feel comfortable with such energy will be attracted to you.

Another effect of a sacred home is that your movements and actions become more careful and graceful. You don't rush through your activities as much. Each act, whether cleaning the stove, going to the bathroom or reading a book, becomes a sacred act because it is being done in a sacred place. Rather than trying to get each job out of the way, we enjoy the simple things of life; we get pleasure from our everyday activities and feel more fulfilled.

2. *Power Objects*

A power object is one with which you have a link of energy. It is an object you hold sacred and which has the ability to alter your energy pattern. A photograph of a loved one is a perfect example. An object you found while on a vacation can remind you of the feelings of that vacation. A work of art or a natural object such as a seashell can fill you with feelings of artistic appreciation. Power objects are usually those which alter your energy pattern in a way that promotes healing or develops certain powers within you.

Quartz crystals are said to be especially good power objects, but almost any object will do as long as it contains your energy and your caring. The trick is to have simple objects in your home be power objects, from decorative knick knacks to the kitchen sink. If you look at the sink and feel disgust because it needs cleaning, then the sink becomes a negative power object causing bad feelings within you. It does not contribute toward the sacredness of your home, but causes ill feeling in you and can contribute to illness.

The solution is not to throw away the sink, but to transform its power so that it enhances your energy pattern by enhancing your feelings. Obviously, you are not doing anything to the sink, but to your own attitude. Yet the method of transforming the sink into a positive power object is to perform a ceremony over it as if you were transforming its energy. Once each object in your home enhances your positive feelings, the home will become a stabilizing, healthy influence in your life. In fact, you may wish to visit natural areas and collect feathers, shells, stones or other objects with which to decorate your home. As each is added to the home, invite it to dwell there with an appropriate ceremony. Entire rooms can be set up to create different energy effects.

Each object in your home may have a different feeling to it. At certain times you may feel drawn to certain objects, just as at certain times you feel drawn to being with certain friends. This shows a particular imbalance in your energy pattern which that particular object or friend can counterbalance. If that imbalance is left untreated, it will weaken the body and can eventually lead to some organic or microbial disease. Working on the energy level in this manner cures a more basic cause of disease, the imbalance in the pattern of energy.

By becoming familiar with the effects of your power objects on your feelings, you will come to know which object should be used at which times. These power objects, then, perform a function similar to medicines, but on an energy level. They are not toxic or habit-forming and act immediately.

Here are some suggestions for power objects:

a. A glass bowl of water filled with naturally colorful pebbles.

b. Parts of animals, such as sea shells, turtle shells and feathers.

c. Tapestries and other cloth art (preferably things you have made).

d. Driftwood.

e. Mineral crystals and rocks.

f. Pottery (with painted designs meaningful to you).

g. A small wooden container housing other power objects.

h. Leather or cloth pouches holding other power objects.

When you are looking for a power object, try to notice how nature is trying to "point out" to you the power object it "wants" you to take. Perhaps, when you eye a particularly nice piece of driftwood, a seagull will bless it with fertilizer just at that moment. Or you may be walking through the woods and notice a snake just shedding its skin. Take this as a sign that nature wants you to have these things.

Even another person can be a power object, or as we say, a "bank of consciousness." As we experiment with different states of consciousness, those we have worked with years before may be forgotten. It is therefore important to share your states of consciousness with others working in the same manner. In this way, if you are out of touch with a particular state of consciousness or energy pattern, you can consult another person who has this particular pattern at his fingertips. It may have been you who showed him this particular pattern, and he may have retained it while you lost it. That person is then a bank of consciousness for you. You have deposited an energy pattern in another person, just as you deposit money in a bank, only to withdraw it later when you need it.

Religions are also banks of consciousness, for they teach people to achieve a particular state. Cultures are banks of consciousness. T'ai-chi is not quite like this, as it teaches you how to experiment with many states and does not limit you to just one.

3. *Form and Emptiness*

If your home is filled with objects of little or even negative feelings to you, then from an energy perspective it is cluttered and can be harmful to your energy.

If you look at a natural scene, you will notice a balance between objects (mountains, trees, etc.) and emptiness (vast expanses of sky, the surface of water). This balance is one of the important elements which makes a natural scene seem beautiful and peaceful to us. This same balance is necessary within our own lives and homes. Don't be afraid of empty space. It can be as beautiful as the single object placed within it. Each enhances the other. The object makes the emptiness stand out even more, while the empty space does the same for the object.

Within our own lives, emptiness is essential as well. It is said that the mind should be like an empty, fertile field. If a seed drops to the earth, normally it grows rapidly and well. But if the field is filled with weeds, that seed will never have a chance to grow. The mind needs rest just as the body does. Even our stomachs need rest. If we were to stuff them all day long, our health would soon suffer.

If this principle of balance between form and emptiness, or activity and rest, is to become incorporated into our lives, we must use it in setting up our homes. The balance between objects and empty space will influence a similar balance within us and create a feeling of peace and harmony which will keep us healthy. A small vase with a single flower set on a large countertop is an example of such harmony.

Examine the various objects in your home and decide which are necessary and which are excess. Let go of the excess. This will simplify your life. When you have done this for objects, go on to activities, habits and beliefs. Bring a balance of form and emptiness into each area of your life. In this manner, all sorts of tensions will be released as your life becomes simpler. Such tensions weaken the body and make it easy to get sick.

4. *Randomness*

Natural scenery is random. Trees do not grow in rows; mountains are not square or rectangular. There are few examples of perfect triangles, circles or other geometric shapes in nature. The randomness of nature is very pleasing to us and creates a feeling of freedom and spontaneity.

Most of us have geometrically perfect rooms: squares, rectangles, or even circles. But within our rooms, we can create a feeling of natural randomness. This doesn't mean sloppiness. (I can visualize some readers emptying their dressers and throwing their clothes around the house.) The arrangement of furniture, plants, rugs, pictures, etc., can be done in such a way as to give the impression of randomness. Zen masters often have their pictures slightly tilted and off-center on the wall for the same reason. While a tilted picture may seem a bit extreme, try placing it toward one end of the wall rather than at the center.

Painters often use the principle of the golden mean. Their center of attention is not placed at the center of the canvas, but one-third of the way to the right or left and one-third of the way to the top or bottom. The eye of the observer must be allowed to wander along certain paths created by the artist. If the painting were perfectly geometrical, the observer's eye would not move and the painting would be uninteresting.

Notice the way in which your attention flows as you enter your home. Does it flow smoothly or is it jarred by the arrangement of objects in the room? The effect of the room on your attention is very influential to your state of health. Become the artist of your own home and make adjustments to allow your attention to travel smoothly about each room.

5. *Colors*

Use colors as a painter does, considering the effects of those colors on creating a positive atmosphere for you. Red, orange and yellow are associated with warmth, while greens and blues are associated with healing and coolness (green with fertility). Vivid colors are energizing, while soft colors are peaceful. But you decide what these colors mean to you.

Never merely accept the colors or set-up of a room when you move into it. This would be the same as accepting any food or drug, no matter how harmful. There are people who do accept these things with little thought, but they are not Taoist magicians. Notice the way in which sunlight enters your windows at various times of the day. Take this into consideration when arranging the rooms. Perhaps you can place a flower vase in a place where the setting sun casts an orange glow. Or several brightly colored seashells can be placed on a shelf hit by the full force of the noonday sun. Color and sunlight add vigor and liveliness to a home, and these qualities will pervade the personality and energy patterns of people living in that home.

With the above principles in mind, you can transform your home into a center of healing far more effective than any hospital. The addition of natural sounds (from a tape recorder) such as bird songs, waves, a stream, even children playing at a beach, will create an atmosphere which will keep you healthy.

Principles of Nature

We often ignore the effects of our external surroundings on our internal state. In our advanced technological societies we need not fear tigers lurking behind trees. Our senses are therefore not sharply attuned to the environment. Those who live in wilderness areas (or in modern inner cities) can feel when danger is lurking, even when it is not visible or audible. Subconsciously, they avoid areas of danger. There is a connection to the environment more subtle than through the senses with which we are familiar. While our lives have been made fairly safe and comfortable, this connection to the environment is essential to our health.

For millions of years, our species has evolved in natural areas and our bodies, emotions and even our minds are a product of nature. The fact that we now drive around in cars or fly in planes does not change our basic biological nature. By examining the natural principles governing our behavior as a biological species, we can gain insights into how our external environment affects our internal state, our energy pattern.

1. *Triggers*

Programmed within us is a species memory, a composite picture of all the factors in our environment which can aid or destroy us. All animals have this. A duckling responds to the shadow of a bird flying overhead. If the neck of the shadow is long, the duckling's species memory tells it that the bird is a duck or a goose. If the neck is short, the bird may be a hawk or an eagle, which can eat ducklings, and so the duckling flees.

There are thousands of these "cues" in the environment for humans as well. They trigger responses within us. Some of these responses are external in the sense that we respond with observable behavior. Some trigger chemical changes within the body, as anyone can experience during springtime.

If you are not aware of these effects, you may fail to respond to them, thereby denying your body the chance to harmonize with the environment. If you are not sensitive to the approach of winter, for example, your body may fail to develop a thin layer of fat to protect you from the cold. You will then be in a weakened state, unable to withstand the cold.

I take advantage of every snowstorm to go for a long walk while the winds are still howling. This drives home to my body the realization that it is winter, and the body makes the proper adjustments. At the first winter storm, I bundle up and sit in my gazebo, watching the lightning.

Campfires are powerful triggers. For tens of thousands of years, our species has been sitting around the evening campfire, usually in groups of twenty-five or less. Watching a campfire with friends stirs deep species memories within us, linking us to our biological past. Fire provided warmth, protection from animals, cooking and smelting of metals. Fire was used to stampede animals to make them easier to corner and catch for food.

The campfire, or in modern times, the candle of religious ceremonies, is a symbol of unity, survival and power. Lighting a candle in the center of a circle of friends can trigger these feelings within you and can actually energize you. As a symbol of power and protection, it can be used whenever you are in a weakened state.

Facial expressions and body movements are also triggers. When another person responds aggressively, it's natural for you to react to that aggressiveness. But sometimes a person can send you mixed signals. His voice may be soothing and pleasant, but the implications of his words and his body posture may be aggressive. The bank foreclosure official may be very pleasant as he explains why he is throwing you out of your home. Yet there may be several police officers standing by, ready to beat you over the head if you should resist. Your body would then be responding in two different ways: to the pleasantness of the bank representative and to the unpleasantness of the situation. The same is true in many situations all around us. Our bodies are protected from attack and starvation for the most part, yet the artificiality of our environment, of our time schedule and interpersonal relations, is an offense to our basic nature.

Luckily, there is such a teaching as T'ai-chi-Ch'uan, which develops the natural part of yourself as much as books and classrooms develop the intellectual part. Push Hands and Kung-Fu place you in situations which call for the maximum in awareness, reaction time and stamina and yet (with proper protection in the case of Kung-Fu) they do not cause serious injury. The Form develops balance, gracefulness, flexibility and concentration.

2. *Interdependence*

The more we learn about nature, the more we find out how intricate living systems are. On this planet are millions of species containing billions of individuals each. Within each creature are trillions of cells and within them a staggering number of molecules.

And yet, with all this complexity, the whole system seems to work. The planet does not need oil changes or tune-ups. (Although some say the planet is about to undero a major geological change, a planetary tune-up, as it were. More on this in the next chapter.) The entire mechanism is finely balanced, and each organism, each species, each habitat, is a balanced part of the whole. If any one part is upset, the whole suffers.

With the destruction of the great South American rainforests, a different amount of light is being absorbed in that area and a different amount of water evaporating. This is affecting weather patterns around the world. In addition, there will be less oxygen for all of us, as this area was the second largest source of oxygen produced by plants in the world. (The oceans, which are getting more polluted each year, are the primary source of oxygen.)

In a city on mainland China, sparrows were killed by the millions because they left their droppings on the city's statues. Next year the insect population mushroomed, as there were no sparrows to eat them. Much of that year's crop was lost.

In our own bodies, we can see this principle of interdependence at work. Each organ must be working properly in order for the whole organism to function well. Diet, rest, exercise, meditation, shelter, etc., are all vital to maintain health. An improper diet will throw all the cells of the body off their proper functioning. I try to eat the same diet our ancestors have been eating for hundreds of thousands of years: a large amount of vegetables, a small amount of meat, a lot of fruit and, from more recent times, a lot of grain. Our ancestors were opportunists; they ate whatever they could get their hands on that wouldn't eat them back. This included eggs, grubs, roots, berries, etc. (Grubs are *not* included in my diet!)

In the external world, when there is a major unheaval such as an earthquake, some say God has done this to punish us. (Although other creatures in the area are also being punished along with us. What sins did they commit?) But with our own bodies we cannot look outside for the cause of illness. It was not God's decision for you to eat that pepperoni-anchovy-garlic pizza last night before going to sleep. You make the choices which affect your body. Just as you feel helpless in the midst of a tornado or a tidal wave, the cells of your body are helpless in the face of your ill-considered dietary decisions.

Each cell of your body is a little being. It is sensitive to its environment and responds to it. In this manner, it has a form of consciousness, although it is not the same level of consciousness you possess. The cells of the body form an interdependent community of beings, and to them, you are God. You are the next highest level of consciousness.

You have one quality of consciousness which your cells possess in a much lesser degree (if at all) and that is independence. Imagine what would happen if your cells decided to build roads inside you and dams in your blood vessels! Fortunately, they can't. But you can choose to hurt yourself by going against natural harmony. I can imagine the cells of your body praying to you to stop the inflow of pepperoni or to take a rest. That seems comical; yet in a way, your cells do pray to you. The bad feelings you experience when you abuse yourself are the despair of the cells in your body. Those feelings are their tears and their pleading for you to live a healthier life. Do you believe there is a God who listens to your prayers? Do you listen to the prayers of your cells?

Your cells know nothing of your activities as a person. They don't know about movies, for example. Yet, when you watch a car-chase scene in a movie and adrenalin fills your body, the cells are aware of the effects of your movie watching and respond appropriately. Their awareness is of the secondary effects of your activities and they act to maintain harmony and health on that level. Their responsibility is toward their own internal workings and toward the community of cells in which they live. If each cell were to decide to become selfish and go off and do what it wanted to, your body would be a mess. It couldn't function. Luckily, as far as we know, cells do not have independence of action (although if they do, such independence may turn out to be a cause of disease).

This concept may be driven home further when you realize that originally, in evolutionary history, there were no multicellular organisms. Each organism was composed of a single cell. At a certain stage of evolution, several types of cells merged to form the earliest multicellular creatures, each type of cell contributing its abilities to the whole community. Our own bodies, then, are the result of this gathering together of many different types of cells striving to develop a harmonious community.

Can we say the same for ourselves on the organismic level? Do we choose to work for the harmony and health of the entire planet? Obviously not, to a large degree. Our environmental destruction, racism, sexism, intolerance, indifference to the extinction of wildlife species and wars show that we are a danger to the planet as a whole. Most non-technological societies have chosen to remain within their natural spheres of influence. That is, they have chosen to be unobtrusive to the environment and concentrate on keeping their own bodies and minds in good condition. But we have taken on the job of the next higher consciousness, the planet, although we are not really intelligent enough to do so.

Imagine what would happen if our stomach cells decided to run our entire lives. (I myself have been accused of succumbing to this situation.) Such cells would imagine the next level of consciousness (their God) as a super stomach. All things in their world would be perceived in terms of food. Stomach cells are not equipped to handle our lives. We need the entire community of cells to do the job. In a similar manner, the planet needs its many species and wilderness areas to function properly.

If we could listen to our cells, if we could focus our attention down to that level, it would be easier to focus in the other direction as well and be aware of the next higher level. Through T'ai-chi-Ch'uan, we do learn to concentrate on individual cells, to become aware of their condition and how our actions affect them. By developing awareness of our own cells, we can gauge our actions to best maintain our health.

In addition, such sensitivity also allows us to develop a harmonious and conscious relationship with the next higher level of consciousness. Rather than seeing that level as a "big person" (as our stomach cells imagined us to be a big stomach), we take a more community-minded approach. The next level of consciousness is the harmonious balancing system of the planet—the ecology, the natural forces around us. It is the "individual Tao" of the planet. We become a channel between the next higher and lower levels of consciousness and become aware of the relationship between the environment and ourselves and between ourselves and our cells. Rejoined once again to the planetary Tao, we find sources of energy more than sufficient to maintain our health and sources of wisdom to maintain harmonious human relationships as well.

This does not imply that we must give up our independence and personal will. Rather, we learn how to use that will to live our lives more harmoniously. T'ai-chi people are among the most independent characters you will ever meet, yet they are also among the most ecologically- and community-minded people.

To continue to develop scientifically and yet end our destruction of the environment is one of the greatest challenges of this generation. If we fail, we will fail for all time. And that will be a failure of health on a grand scale!

3. *Cycles*

The symbol of T'ai-chi is the Yin/Yang symbol—a circle containing what seem to be two fish drawn so as to completely fill the circle. Where the tail of one fish thins out to a point, the head of the other fish fills in the circle. The two fish seem to be circling one another. One fish is black with a white eye, while the other is white with a black eye. The cyclic principle of nature is depicted here, the circle surrounding the fishes showing that the whole of nature is composed of these two complementary energies. The black eye of the white fish and the white eye of the black fish show that within each end of a cycle lies the seed of the complementary aspect of that cycle.

Within our bodies are many cycles which are the bases of the proper functioning of our bodies. Cells grow, reproduce through division into daughter cells, then grow again. The blood picks up oxygen and releases carbon dioxide into the lungs, then travels through the body to release the oxygen and pick up more waste. There are cycles of waking, sleeping, eating and fasting. The list could go on almost endlessly.

But let's take a look at some cycles we don't normally pay much attention to. Breathing is cyclic, for we breathe in and out. Proper breathing is essential for good health, yet few of us breathe properly. T'ai-chi-Ch'uan pays a great deal of attention to breathing. Learning to breathe, while it sounds absurd, is a major component of the teaching.

We learn that our breathing should be as smooth and even as the Yin/Yang symbol. When we begin to breathe in a slow, smooth manner, we notice that all sorts of negative feelings, both physical and emotional, seem to be washed away. the mind calms down. Nervousness and hyperactivity fade away. This one change, that of smoothing out and slowing down the breath, has an enormous impact on our well-being. With the Form, we learn to coordinate proper breathing with physical movement, so that we may breathe properly all day.

Another cycle is the expansion and focusing of attention. This is a cycle rarely discussed. Just as the body needs a balance of rest and activity, it also needs a balance of focused and expanded attention. We call these two aspects "linear" and "spherical" (or "holographic"). Linear attention focuses on only one subject at a time. It's like the focused light of a laser beam. This is the type of attention used in thinking. Spherical attention is diffuse, like a spider's web. It is everywhere at once. In this state you feel connected to your entire world.

There is a cycle to attention, just as there is a cycle to breathing. If you try to use your attention in one way while it is in the opposite phase, you will be wasting your time. In modern society, the linear phase is emphasized almost to the exclusion of the spherical. This interference with a natural cycle is as detrimental as interfering with breathing or the flow of blood. I find that interference with this cycle produces anger and agitation, much as in a person who has not had enough rest for a long time.

The T'ai-chi-Ch'uan student quickly becomes aware of this cycle by the use of the breathing Forms and Chi-Gung. And while we can play with this cycle, extending one aspect or the other or consciously switching to the complementary aspect, we never try to eliminate either side of the cycle permanently. Just as we may choose to stay up late, only to sleep later in the morning, we can extend one side of the consciousness cycle only if we make up for it at another time. When a society tries to eliminate one side of the cycle of consciousness permanently, it dooms its members to ill health.

There is another cycle which this society and others have affected in a strange way. According to the principle of Yin/Yang, there are within our bodies many balancing cycles of energies. One of these cycles is that of masculine and feminine behavior. Within each of us are feelings of tenderness and roughness, passivity and aggressiveness. With a logic as senseless as it is destructive, we have singled out one of these energies for women and another for men. This makes about as much sense as allowing men to only breathe out and women to only breathe in. Luckily this attitude is now changing, women allowing themselves to be more aggressive and men allowing themselves to be more tender. Some years ago, the concept of androgyny was developed, suggesting that a balance of male and female energies is necessary in each of us. (Of course, this concept has been around for thousands of years in other cultures.) After all, women naturally have some male hormones and men, some female hormones. Each of us has a wide variety of feelings because we are complex organisms trying to live in harmony with a complex world. But society has made a shopping list of feelings and allows each of us only a few.

Even in some Taoist practices the concept of Yin/Yang has been warped (in my opinion). There is a Taoist yogic teaching which suggests that in order to achieve long life and even immortality, one must avoid achieving orgasm during sex, while trying to get the partner to do so. In this sexual competition, one partner tries to steal vital life energy from the other. By also using imagery and Chi-Gung breathing techniques, a spiritual "golden pill" is developed, a cosmic embryo which enables a person to live for thousands of years.

The secrets of this method are said to be hidden symbolically in ancient texts. But I believe that this form of sexual Taoist yoga is in itself symbolic and refers to some of the teachings described in this book. (More on this in the next chapter). I'm quite happy being a natural creature and have no intention of trying to "cheat" nature. I've found that nature is even smarter than I am, and when I try to cheat it by going against the natural way of things, I usually wind up suffering for it. To my way of thinking, it is perfectly natural for both partners in sex to achieve orgasm. You have to be careful to separate the basic principles of a teaching from the way in which they are interpreted.

The basic principles of T'ai-chi teach you to live in harmony with nature. When you try to eliminate or warp the natural cycles of feeling within you, you begin to destroy your self-confidence. If you have the attitude that your natural feelings are bad or must be altered in order to be acceptable, then you are not accepting yourself as a natural, biological creature. You will be engaged in Black Magic, that is, trying to interfere with nature in a destructive way. Once you end the battle against your own inner spirit, you will experience great peace and self-love.

4. *Growth and Decay*

Switching to a larger time-scale, there is the cycle of our own birth, growth, reproduction and death. When we speak of the individual Tao, that energy which forms our structure on all levels, this is not meant to imply that our energy pattern is static. It is a fluid, living energy. The individual Tao of humans goes through a specific series of changes as we grow, similar to the changes our physical body goes through. We grow larger. Our hormones change. We grow intellectually. If these processes are interfered with, our health suffers.

Children are naturally filled with curiosity and wonder. Our educational system too often destroys these qualities, reducing the entirety of the universe to a few facts listed in textbooks. Rather than encouraging curiosity, many school systems promote the attitude that we now know almost everything, while "primitive" cultures are ignorant. Children are taught only one perspective, basically the Newtonian, that the world consists of physical objects bouncing into each other, and that any other perspective is due to ignorance or derangement. Childhood is a time of magic, a time in which free-flowing creativity and imagination should be used to play with the physical world. Children should be taught several perspectives (such as the energy organizing principle), so their minds can remain flexible and tolerant. This is the need of the Tao in the time of youth. If we do not recognize this need, we will stunt the organism from the roots up, just as if it had been malnourished.

Adolescence is a time of experimentation with relationships and a time of communication of feelings. We place many obstacles in the way of this process. Our cultural orientation is toward consumerism, watching TV, following ball-game scores and gossiping about neighbors. These are activities that occupy much of the attention of many people. There is a great lack of discussion about feelings, let alone about living in harmony with the environment.

It is startling to hear the people of a nature-oriented culture talk. While there is certainly some gossip and purchasing of consumer goods, there is also a lot of discussion about nature. An individual's actions are judged not on the basis of a book of etiquette, but on how closely they parallel natural processes. The basic premise of their judgments is harmony with nature, while all too often with us, it is getting away with as much as we can without being caught. The relationships of adolescents in our society become a contest of egos rather than a true opening-up of feelings.

Rock 'n Roll has become a communication medium among young people in the West (and now all over the world). One of the reasons for its strength is that it is feeling-oriented, both in lyrics and music. I believe that one of the reasons it was offensive to those of my parents' generation is that it made them feel more than they were used to feeling. The culture of today is extremely different than that of twenty-five years ago, and one of the greatest differences, in my opinion, is that it is moving in the direction of feeling and away from living exclusively from the mind.

Many people simply do not feel their bodies. When asked to express their emotions, a label comes forth such as sad, happy, angry, etc. Feeling a label is safer than feeling the feeling itself. Feelings are seen as a nuisance by some and the mind as a safe refuge. Take time out right now to feel your feelings. Do not label those feelings or you'll be yanked right up into the realm of mind. Try to notice whether you are caging your feelings or trying to interfere with them in some way. We put so little emphasis on learning about feelings.

The middle years, from the 20's on, are a time of accomplishment in your life, of building a family and/or a career; a time of intellectual, spiritual and emotional growth. With the creativity of childhood and the emotional opening-up of adolescence still intact, middle age is an exciting, adventurous time, a time of exploration and of trying out skills and knowledge in a practical way. It is a time of learning leadership qualities in parenting, business, politics, relationships and your own individual life.

Toward the end of life, senior citizens in many societies are highly respected for their wisdom and experience. In some cases they are given the major responsibility for raising children. They do not dread old age as we do in this country. Their entire attitude toward growing old is different, far more positive.

When the natural cycle of the human Tao is allowed to unfold, there will be little disease. From a study of these principles of nature and how they relate to your own life, you can begin to end your interference with those principles. This will strengthen you and eliminate many causes of disease.

This process is known as Taoist magic. You see yourself as a process of energy and learn how to use that energy to your advantage. You allow the energy within you to harmonize with the energy of the planet.

Ego as Organizing Principle

We've taken a look at the way in which the subject of energy can be used as a central issue around which to organize a theory of illness and well-being. Now we'll look at the most common subject to act as an organizing principle in our lives, that of ego or self-identity. This ego O.P. uses our role in society to understand disease. We all have a certain image of who we are, how we behave, what we believe in and of our relationships with other people. This self-image is as precious to some people as their physical bodies. When choices have to be made whether to maintain health or a certain self-image, the self-image often wins out.

Our self-image is largely influenced by the community we live in. Each community has principles by which to judge the behavior of its members. Respect is given to those who most closely resemble the standard community member. This is true in all cultures. If the respected role consists of drinking large quantities of beer, getting little sleep and abusing the other members, that role will be a cause of poor health and an unhappy life. That is an obvious example. In much subtler ways, the role or roles we have adopted can mean the difference between good health and illness.

Creating Illness

For many years, I perceived myself as a very busy person, constantly rushing around with many things to do. My life was run in a way which created constant work. If I wasn't teaching, I was going to study groups, taking care of a large collection of animals and the garden, writing, reading, volunteering for community groups, etc.

After a few years of T'ai-chi-Ch'uan, I felt I had discovered a way to accomplish all I wished to. The relaxation I developed allowed me to sleep only five or six hours a night. Then I began skipping a night of sleep every other week. I learned to move twice as quickly when I worked so I would get twice as much done. From the moment I woke up to the moment I went to sleep, I didn't rest. I worked 80 hours a week for half the year and 60 hours a week the other half.

At the end of the third year, my body let me know it couldn't keep up the pace. I made a "treaty" with my body: if it held out one more month, I would take it easy after that. When the month was up, there was more work to do, so I broke the treaty. My body went on the warpath. For five days I was laid out with severe back pains so intense I couldn't sleep day or night, but had to concentrate deeply to try to ease the pain. The doctor told me it would take two or three months to recover, but luckily, using T'ai-chi-Ch'uan, it took only three weeks.

I realized that I had abused T'ai-chi-Ch'uan. Instead of using it as the basis for a healthful lifestyle, I had used it to try to cheat nature—to support an unhealthy self-image. My body's lesson was very convincing. I was reminded of the Zen teacher who used to walk up to his students in the hallway holding a stick in his hand.

"Tell me what this is," he would say. "If you say it is a stick, I will hit you thirty times. If you say it is something else, I will hit you thirty times. If you neglect to answer, I will still hit you thirty times. Quick! What is it?"

The only appropriate response, it seems to me, was to take the master's stick away. I felt that my body was holding a stick over my head—the memory of what it did to me and what it could do again. My response was to alter my hectic way of life. On the other hand, I had been holding a stick over my body with overwork and it responded admirably. I am no longer holding that stick over my body. I let it walk the halls of life in peace.

Helplessness

Another damaging self-image is that of being weak and helpless. As a baby, your crying and weakness brought others to help you. But there are some adults who act helpless too. The behavior of waiting for others to do things for you is a standard role for women in this culture. This attitude of helplessness is dangerous because it convinces you that you are not responsible for your own well-being.

Let's take the example of fears, whether they are of snakes, spiders or heights. A fear is a certain feeling. When you see the subject of your fear, your body undergoes tension and other reactions. You feel intense feelings. The fearful person does not want to feel these feelings. Generally, he is afraid to feel altogether.

But in order for fear to have control over your behavior, there must be an underlying assumption of helplessness: "I fear heights and I can't help it." When you let go of this element of your self-image, your attitude changes completely. When the fear arises, you face it and examine it. You refuse to allow it to have power over you. The feelings of fear cannot hurt you. Realizing this, you look forward to the challenge of laughing at the fear. As for the object of fear, whether a utility bill or a Kung-Fu fighter, the T'ai-chi student faces it immediately with whatever ability he has at his disposal. If his ability is meager, he uses that small amount of ability with confidence. Winning and losing is no longer his concern, so his ego is able to step aside and allow the BM to practice projecting its power into the world through his life. Helplessness is a role you learn to play in order to prevent BM from exercising its power.

T'ai-chi-Ch'uan teaches you to experience fear as a pattern of energy (or really, a warping of the pattern) and to let go of that fear. Letting go of fear does not mean pushing it away. It means that when you experience those feelings, you no longer put a negative connotation on them. You don't try to run away from them, but you don't try to grab hold of them either. The feelings which you interpret as fear are allowed to come and go as they please. You soon realize that the fear is really an act of mind—a labeling of intense feelings as negative.

Why is it that the reptile house is the most crowded exhibit at zoos, even though reptiles are feared? It's because the sight of reptiles creates strong feelings in people. We say that they possess an intense energy, and in most cultures snakes have been and still are revered (from American Indians and China to ancient Egypt and pagan Europe). It's this intensity of feelings that is fearful to people who say they are afraid of snakes. People need to experience intense feelings. That's why they visit the reptile house and roller-coaster rides. The blockage of intense feelings warps their energy patterns and contributes to disease.

To accept the premise that you are really not helpless is very difficult. I had studied ways to neutralize burns merely by doing Chi-Gung breathing exercises. One day I accidentally spilled a pot of boiling water over my hand. I was about to reach for ice for my injured hand when I remembered the breathing exercises. There was an instant of indecision. But I knew I had to act as I believed, and I believed I was not helpless, that merely through this breathing technique I could prevent a burn.

So I tried it. I took the chance that my hand might be severely injured as a statement that I was not helpless. Luckily, the technique worked. I've used it ever since for burns and other problems. But each time I use it, there is still a part of me that says, "This can't work." It is the self-image of helplessness which still hasn't been completely eradicated.

I believe we rely too heavily on doctors and don't give our bodies enough credit for being powerful self-healers. We are taught to be dependent. Helplessness is often thought of as being sexy in a woman. To me it's not sexy; it's destructive and one of the causes of disease.

Winning and Losing

Winning and losing is another attitude which can be detrimental to health. I have already mentioned how, in T'ai-chi-Ch'uan, the attitude of winning out over the opponent is changed to that of harmonizing with the partner. The attitude of life as a series of battles which must be won has serious health effects and shows how the structure of self-identity can be a cause of disease.

Biologically, a whole series of chemical reactions occurs within our bodies when the organism is faced with overcoming a difficult situation. The body immediately prepares to fight or take flight. Energy stores and hormones such as adrenalin are released into the bloodstream. The nervous system is put on hair-trigger sensitivity. Such a reaction is quite healthy and natural. Engaging in exhausting competitive sports on a regular basis will build stamina, awareness and a general feeling of well-being. But when we perceive every moment of our lives as being a battle, this same bodily reaction takes place constantly. The nervous system never returns to a state of rest. Energy stores are used up quickly, and the hormonal balance of the body is upset.

It is very tempting to view life as a series of problems to be overcome, because so often that seems to be the case. When our lives are going well, we wonder what trouble is brewing. Yet we know that this attitude hurts the body and that in order to live healthy lives, we must stop hurting ourselves. Our constant worrying wears us out and does little to solve the problem.

Dropping the Battles

But luckily, we are not helpless creatures. We have the power to change our lives immediately and decisively for the sake of our health. Here are several techniques for dropping the "life as battles" attitude:

1. When you catch yourself thinking about a problem you have, decide whether thinking about it at that time will solve the problem. Often such thought becomes repetitive and no new solutions are forthcoming. Unless thinking about it can solve the problem within a short time, drop the thinking. Realize that it is the creative part of yourself, BM, which usually comes up with the solutions and the BM does not work by thinking. Pay attention only to the things going on right in front of you. It may take some time to be able to do this, but the health rewards are great.

2. Think about death. That is, think about all you have, all you are experiencing which you would not be experiencing if you had never been born. Accept life as a gift which didn't have to be given to you. When you base your life on winning, all the experiences you have short of winning will not be appreciated. When winning ceases to by your main goal in life, you will be able to appreciate *all* your experiences.

Just as the T'ai-chi student is surprised at the maneuvers he is able to come up with, you will be surprised each time you do "win" because it will be BM, working behind the scenes, which has set you up to win. Let BM win for you. You just enjoy being alive, whatever you may feel life has dealt you.

3. Realize that your ego doesn't have the power to win all your battles. BM is your greatest ally. When the mind stops trying to do it all by itself and enlists the aid of BM, it won't have to fight so hard. Call on your ally, BM, and trust that in time it will take care of your needs. BM is a creature of the earth and can, in turn, call upon the earth creature to come to its aid. What force can then stand in your way? If you deal with life only through mind, you're setting yourself up to lose. Then life will indeed seem like a series of battles.

4. Ask yourself these questions: "What do I really want?"; "What do I really feel?"; "What do I want this minute?"; "What do I feel right now?" Often, when I ask people what they feel, they give me their opinions. They don't even know how to feel; the closest they can come to feeling is thinking. But in this exercise, determine how your body feels. Then determine what your important

needs are *at that moment*. You may be fighting a battle to win a prize you don't even want. Your mind might want it, but it may be of little value for your well-being. And fighting the battle to get it may be harmful.

Are you battling to protect your self-image in the eyes of others? What is this self-image? Of what value is it? You may spend your life like the guard at the gates of a walled city, battling all who wish to get in, because you believe there is some valuable treasure inside. And yet you don't really know what lies inside. How many of us have really examined what lies within our walls? Is it a treasure others can steal? Open those doors and take a look inside. You may find that it is an empty room, the greatest treasure of all, a treasure no one can steal.

Why is an empty room the greatest treasure? The Zen and Taoist teachers point to the bowl which, in its very emptiness, is of great use, for it holds the soup for you to eat. Should the bowl be filled with ceramic, no soup would fit therein. When you are empty of unending desire, when you stop trying to win over others in a mad rush to grab as much of everything as possible, then you can have the entire universe for your own. For who can take away from you the stars in the sky, the laughter of children in your ears? When your desires are simple, they are easy to fulfill. And then you can partake of the greatest treasures this life has to offer without so much as one battle.

You may want more money than is necessary to live a peaceful, healthy life, so that you can buy certain things. Yet the extra work and time necessary to acquire that money may wear you down to the point of illness. Check to see where that desire is coming from. Whose needs are you satisfying, the needs of the ego or those of the entire organism? Who is serving whom? Who do you think you are?

5. Learn to choose your beliefs. You may believe that the world is evil or a series of battles. Did you choose that belief? Where did that belief come from? Is that belief serving you? How does it help you? Don't worry about whether it's true or false. Learn to use beliefs. You don't have to have your rationality's permission to have a belief. Just take some time out to understand the effects of your beliefs on your life. If those effects are harmful, feel free to change your beliefs as you would change any other harmful habit.

6. When a battle comes up in your life, try to determine how that battle came into being. The attitude that life is only a series of battles creates those very battles. If you look to the environment to find battles, you are sure to find them. You will be structuring your life to enable your ego to fight and win. Accept responsibility for your own life to the extent that you accept your role in your life's battles. A Taoist magician doesn't try to fix blame on others, but believes that he creates his own life and that he can change it through his awareness and willpower.

One of these battles is sickness. When you get sick, this is perceived as losing a battle. The T'ai-chi view is that you have won the battle. You've been trying to make yourself sick by your way of living and you have succeeded. The question is, what battle are you fighting and whose side are you on? An examination of your goals and priorities in life is essential to good health.

Enthusiasm for Life

The old cry, "What is the meaning of life?" contains within it the assumption that somebody has the secret and that you must discover it. As a creative person, you create your own meanings and purposes in life. You don't wait around for someone to tell you what they are. There's always somebody around who is more than willing to tell you what you should do and how to live your life. Advertisers insist that your purpose in life is to buy their products; the military, to fight their wars; and the landlord, to pay him rent. It is hard to sort out what you yourself really want to do with your life. If your goal is to satiate yourself with as much pleasure as you can stuff into your mouth, entice into your bed or sniff into your nose, you will need more and more of these pleasures to satisfy you and will soon turn into a protoplasmic Hefty bag for orgasms and drugs. If your purpose in life is only to work or sustain your ego or think great thoughts, this is equally one-sided.

It is hard to sustain your enthusiasm for life under such conditions. And such enthusiasm is vital to good health. You feel much healthier when you look forward to some new activity, rather than when all you can look forward to is the "same old grind." The "will to live" is recognized by doctors as a major factor—if not *the* major factor—in pulling a patient through a period of illness. If the patient gives up, if he feels defeated and helpless, this feeling in itself may lead to his death. Examine yourself for any feelings of defeat. Is there something which is essential to your well-being (either physical or emotional) that you have lost hope of obtaining? Experience what effect this feeling of defeat has had on your life, on your internal state. Use your will-power for a moment to trust that if you can contact your BM, you can ask it to obtain this important thing for you. Remember that BM is only interested in your basic well-being and knows nothing of fancy cars and million-dollar bank accounts. Ask it for something it is familiar with. Talk to it out loud, though this may seem foolish to you. Combine your willpower and emotions into a piercing, mushrooming laser beam of energy and then let it go. Learn to use that type of energy to fulfill your simple needs.

This will to live is an enthusiasm for life, an energy which has healing qualities: it is chi. As a Taoist magician, you learn to develop a strong, firm chi. Your purpose in life is to create a work of art and that art is your very life. The painter is BM and the paint is chi. Your canvas is the world in which you live. The beautiful picture you create is the result of the harmonious blending of the paints on the canvas. It is your character, your inner being, you attempt to develop rather than the amount of money in your bank account or the number of facts in your mind. Health and well-being, a life of balance and harmony, become your goals. You are a powerful creature. If you work toward health, you will achieve it. If your enthusiasm is determined by your state of health and your personal development, then your life will be doubly blessed.

The Battle for Your Consciousness

There is a battle being waged for your consciousness. As a child, your status among your friends was determined by conforming to a set of standards. Perhaps those standards included strength for boys and beauty for girls. As you grew up, you found yourself faced with many expectations which you hardly understood and rarely questioned. You learned from an early age that questioning the status quo was not approved of by those controlling the resources upon which you depended (whether physical or in terms of peer approval). Surviving in this society required learning its perspectives. The concept of time, the separation of conscious from subconscious awareness, the separation of the dream state from the waking state, were all cultural changes you went through as a child.

You were taught that the different aspects of your personality were all one person. Some children have imaginary playmates, perceiving the various personality patterns as separate individuals. In some cultures, these patterns are seen as separate entities and can be distinguished by a person throughout his life. Among shamanistic cultures they are called power animals and in T'ai-chi, energy patterns.

Each culture has a way of ordering the identity of its citizens and the world they perceive. Of course, the individuals in each culture believe that all people must perceive the world as they do. If anyone has a different perception, he is called "crazy" or "primitive." The manner in which a culture teaches its citizens to identify themselves is a basic determinant of their health. Culture, then, can be a cause of disease.

Multiple Realities

In T'ai-chi, since creativity is perceived as the basic identity of a person, you are free to accept and "try out" each cultural form of identity. With creativity itself as your identity rather than any particular form or structure, you can play around with how you perceive your identity and the world around you, trying out each culture, so to speak.

Thus you can experiment with how any particular structure affects your health and well-being. If a particular structure is causing poor health, you can alter that structure for your own purposes. For example, you can learn to dissolve the barrier between the waking and sleeping states, remaining fully conscious while dreaming. You learn to influence your dreams as a director directs a movie. In the dream state, you concentrate on your nervous system, examining how your internal state influences your dreams. You also examine how your energy pattern is represented as images in dreams. By doing this, you learn to use dreams as a gauge of your state of health.

When you are awake, you can do the Form and slip into the dream state. In this manner, you are in two states at once: you are awake doing the Form and asleep dreaming. At this time, you can examine the way in which the changing flow of internal energy created by doing the Form affects your dreams. At a certain point, it's difficult to tell whether you are in fact awake or asleep. It's extremely important to do so, for if you are not at work but only dreaming you are at work, it's better to stop and do something more enjoyable. But if you are awake and actually at work, it's better to continue working.

To determine whether you are awake or asleep, you do the Form. If your weight flows down through your legs, you are upright and awake. If your weight flows to one side, you are lying in a bed. But after awhile it's hard to tell, because the feeling of your weight begins to flow downward even during dreaming. At that point, it doesn't matter whether you are awake or asleep anymore, because you become involved in another level of awareness in which the dichotomy of dreaming/waking doesn't exist.

Another example of trying out another perspective is dissolving the concept of "self/other." People usually don't perceive the physical world (other than their own bodies) as being part of themselves. You can experiment with perceiving the world of the senses (a tree, for example) as being as much a part of yourself as your body or your thoughts. While you are experimenting with it, the tree will truly be yourself. Thus, you learn to become so flexible that you can deal with what you feel are the true causes of disease. You don't blame the microbes, but take the responsibility onto yourself, like a true magician. If there are aspects of your culture which contribute to disease, you can alter that culture for your betterment.

Lifestyle

One of the first steps in this process of experimentation is to free yourself to some extent from the hold of our present culture on your life. Most of us choose to live within our traditional communities, but some people go to extremes, setting up different independent communities. Networks of like-minded people meet each week or month or "when the moon is full." Within their group, they can operate in a different mode, reinforcing an alternative culture they feel is more compatible with their well-being. The number of such groups in this country runs into the thousands. Luckily, our culture is fairly tolerant of subcultures.

Within your own life you can also set aside time to "practice" an alternative culture. Such practice is called ritual, whether it be the Passover *seder* of the Jews, their lighting of candles on Friday night, saying grace over food among Christians, the smudging of the American Indians or the Forest Wine Ceremony of the Taoists. Ritual connects you to your alternative culture and serves as a way of creating a certain time-period within which you wish to shed the prevailing culture.

Identification with an alternative culture also serves to give you the courage to free yourself from the hold of the prevailing culture. You may call yourself a Taoist or a health-food person or an ecologist. Labeling yourself with an identity which sums up your perspective is like creating a landmark you can look to whenever you get lost in the maze of everyday life. This label is a symbol of your lifestyle. You can also use physical symbols. A picture of the Yin/Yang, an altar for rituals, posters of wildlife, a "save-the-whales" patch on your jacket, all serve to reinforce your commitment to a more healthy way of life.

Once you have freed yourself from a culture you feel is harmful in some way, you're ready to create a new culture based on what you feel are healthier principles. Pick one healthful activity such as the Form, swimming, tree climbing, yoga, etc., and practice it every day at the same time. Coordinate this activity with the natural cycles (sunrise or sunset, for example). This will become the foundation of a more natural way of life. Don't try to do too much at first. A half-hour or even fifteen minutes a day is fine as long as it is done consistently.

Wait until you feel the effects of this activity, so that your body will be convinced of its importance. Then add other healthful activities to your life. At the same time, older activities may have to be dropped to make room for the new ones. Spend a week writing down how each day is spent, how much time you spend on each activity. Work on this list, rearranging or even dropping activities which do not contribute to your well-being. This may be difficult to do, as all your activities may seem important to you. In that case, work from the other end first. Insert the healthful activities first. You'll probably find that your other activities will adjust themselves after awhile.

Making Choices

The skill of making choices as to how you spend your time is one of the greatest powers of a magician. We try not to let these choices be made for us by others. You may be poor, you may be limited by certain conditions (such as the loss of an arm or a leg), but within those limitations, your skill in making choices gives you power.

Exercise that skill with your time schedule. Don't accept any limitations without question. Figure out what sacrifices have to be made to go beyond each limitation. I recently had to sacrifice spending a lot of time with certain friends. I enjoyed their company, and although they had many good qualities as well, I felt they were negative, problem-oriented people who sapped my energy. It was better for both sides that I stopped seeing them. But it was extremely difficult to tell them I didn't want to see them anymore; it caused pain on both sides. My choice had to be based on the long-term well-being of all of us. Once you know the choice you have to make, it still takes strength of will to make it and to accept the consequences. You may have to cut out one of your jobs and therefore make less money, in order to have time to rest. You won't be able to buy that fancy car or eat steak, but you'll feel healthier and enjoy life more.

On what basis do you make your choices? Look at your symbol. Remember the principles of your life and you'll find the way to make your choices. Perhaps what is important to you is your health, treating other people well, your family, learning, sharing your love, protecting the earth, etc. Examine each choice you make on the basis of your own principles. Sometimes your choices are made by habits of behavior programmed into you by your culture. Free yourself from such tyranny. You may make mistakes in your choice-making, but don't come down hard on yourself. Making choices is a skill which must be learned and it takes time to gain that skill. Accept the responsibility for your mistakes and learn from them. Learning to make choices in life is more important to your health than taking aspirin.

One choice I made was to stop watching TV. I felt the programs did not enrich my life and used up valuable time. I gave up the temporary satisfaction of eating foods with sugar and of drinking coffee. These choices had a tremendous impact on my happiness.

Giving Up Manipulation

Another choice I made was to avoid trying to manipulate people to do my bidding. I found this had a dramatic effect on my health. First, I would not feel free to say what I felt if I were manipulative. I would have to calculate the effect of my every word on the listener. Second, I would fall into a web of falsehood and might never find my way out. This confusion would sap my strength. This decision not to manipulate was made at the age of four and is one of my strongest childhood memories. I have never regretted that decision. My energy is not wasted trying to force my will on others and I don't build up resentment when they don't respond to my manipulation. When I want something, I can express it openly and don't feel that my needs have to be hidden, that others have to be tricked into helping me. All that intrigue creates inner turmoil and is a cause of disease.

Simply being straightforward with others and honestly admitting your feelings can make your life a lot easier. This one act will strengthen you more than almost any other as you change to a health-oriented lifestyle. Giving up playing mind games is a sacrifice to some, but it's the type of sacrifice that brings great emotional wealth. Generally, if you play games with others, you're also playing games with yourself. Thus you may be unaware of your real needs. Working on the external world (not playing games with others) can serve to clear your internal world (you'll stop playing games with yourself). When your real needs are clear to you, they are easier to satisfy. The very desire to manipulate may be a cover-up for the need to be honest and open. But we have lots of strange thoughts inside us. You may feel that you don't deserve to have your needs met.

As children, we assume that everybody but us knows what's going on, so we try to figure out the world all by ourselves. Children often cannot talk about their feelings. First of all, we live in a society which does not promote such discussion. Second, it's a competitive society in which knowledge, like other commodities, is not readily shared. If a child admits he doesn't know something, he may be ridiculed. Third, this society does not recognize certain feelings (such as that of energy) and has no words to express them. The child has no way of communicating without the proper words. Even with the words, a child is not yet skilled at verbal communication. And fourth, if no one around him talks about such feelings, he may eventually forget all about them.

So we have grown up with many odd ideas about the world. T'ai-chi-Ch'uan allows you to let go of the entire structure of mind. Your attention is freed from this structure and can examine it from "the outside." From this vantage point, the structure can be rearranged. You begin to see how you yourself have built your own little world and have hidden yourself inside it. Once freed, you can exercise your psychological and emotional muscles and release all the cramps in your energy pattern. You can be honest and straightforward because you have nothing to hide anymore, either from yourself or others.

The Role of T'ai-chi-Ch'uan in Maintaining Health

By the end of the first year of T'ai-chi-Ch'uan practice, most of your tension has dissipated. This tension robs your body of energy and constricts blood vessels. The cells of your body receive less blood and therefore less food and oxygen. The body's wastes cannot be eliminated as quickly and these wastes poison the body. By eliminating excess tension, the body begins to recover from what may be many years of starvation, suffocation and poisoning.

As a muscle is relaxed, you can feel a rush of blood flowing through that area. You can feel the yearning of the cells for the inflow of oxygen and food and for the first time realize how much you have deprived your own body.

T'ai-chi Massage

T'ai-chi massage, a form of accupressure, helps to dissolve muscle tension and nerve trauma. There is a fundamental difference between these two forms of massage. In accupressure the student is trained through a study of the accupressure points and performs particular techniques on particular muscles.

T'ai-chi massage is quite different. You learn to feel the flow of energy with your palms and to recognize when the energy is blocked or warped. You then respond to the particular needs in each area of the person being massaged, without using any pre-set technique. Your method of massaging comes from Push Hands. Just as you work with the flow of momentum between yourself and a partner, you do the same with the muscles, but in this case you work with the flow of chi. The muscle becomes your partner and you communicate with it through the nonverbal Push Hands game. You sense how it is responding to your massage and adjust the massage, second to second, as you adjust your movements in Push Hands.

The sensitivity of the muscle, its little consciousness, responds to your massage. Gradually it realizes (in its own way) that it is being addressed and recognized as a conscious being and it begins to wake up. It is as if someone were resting in a chair and we called out his name. He would raise his head and say, "What?" The muscles and nerves within our bodies are often in an unconscious state. The lines of internal communication of the body have been deadened by the repression of feelings. T'ai-chi massage stimulates the cellular and muscle consciousness and opens the lines of communication.

The person being massaged pays attention to the massage and is aware on a conscious level of the communication going on between his body and the masseur. He can then open lines of communication between his body and mind. As the masseur, though, your thinking mind is not really involved in the massage. Rather, it is your BM, through the sensitivity in your fingers, which does the massage. Your hands have a consciousness of their own and you find them going automatically to the proper place on the body. You must give your hands free reign, as a flutist's fingers seem to dance about the flute by themselves. Through T'ai-chi massage, the mind and body of the client begin to open up to each other and develop a harmonious relationship.

T'ai-chi massage is not painful. The feeling of the release of deep-seated tension and trauma is extremely pleasurable. A common description of the massage is, "My body finally feels really alive!" It energizes the body, yet calms it as well. Negative feelings seem to be washed away and the senses become more alert. When people emerge from such a massage, they all seem to have the same expression. There is a dazed look on their faces and a huge smile. They seem to be drifting among the clouds.

Many Health Benefits

Just as the energy lines of communication are opened up within the body, so are they opened between the body and the planet. Just as there is a need for a free flow of blood within the body, there is a need for the free flow of energy between the body and the environment. Your energy level is not easily depleted then, for new energy is constantly flowing in. In addition, by doing the Form, you learn to use only the minimum amount of energy necessary for each action, so you don't use up much energy. Push Hands teaches you not to resist force, which also conserves energy.

This relaxed, passive state also has another advantage. When negative energy is directed against you, it just passes through you, for you don't resist it. Such energy merely passes down through your root and into the earth. American Indians will bury themselves in the earth for a time to get rid of negative energy. We simply ground it through the root.

T'ai-chi-Ch'uan increases the flexibility of the body, imparting a springy, youthful character to its movements. The posture is relaxed, as in a child, and allows more room for the organs, releasing pressure on those organs. There are also T'ai-chi techniques for preventing burns and blisters and for sending healing energy to any part of the body.

Kung-Fu increases stamina and reaction time and releases deep-seated emotional fears. Push Hands trains you to base your life on the principle of Yin/Yang, balance and counterbalance, which is called the "middle path" in other cultures because you are not living at either extreme. Push Hands also addresses what I feel to be one of the main sources of illness in our culture—the fear of touching. This is not a "touching-caring" culture. It's often hard to find human warmth; many people resort to the singles scene, if only to find some comfort for one night. Push Hands is so much a touching game that people are often shocked to see it. While there are certainly no sexual connotations to it (it's not "Push Glands"), an openness and a caring feeling is essential in order to play it. In some T'ai-chi schools, though, I have seen Push Hands based on tension and keeping the other person away from you. This is certainly not our style at the Long Island School of T'ai-chi-Ch'uan. The ability to touch and to care is powerful medicine.

The Form develops gracefulness and a feeling of peace. It frees your attention from the jerky movements of the thinking process and allows it to operate in a smooth, graceful manner. By slowly and carefully releasing BM from its cage of repression and integrating it with the mind, T'ai-chi-Ch'uan ends one of the basic conflicts of our lives. By allowing creativity to flourish, it develops the energy of enthusiasm and makes life seem worth living.

Obviously, I have a deep respect for this teaching and for the large number of benefits it provides compared to the small amount of effort it requires. I can't even imagine what my own life would be like without T'ai-chi-Ch'uan, and I have much gratitude for my teachers and for all the teachers throughout history who have preserved and developed it. I find such a wealth of wisdom in this system that I am awed by those who originated it.

Curing Disease

The T'ai-chi method of curing disease differs from the Western method because of the difference between the theories of disease. Actually, we use the same approach to curing a person as in fixing a car. If the car fails to work, we look for the most obvious causes first. Perhaps the battery terminal is dirty or there is a loose wire. A car owner would not rebuild his engine first and look for the simpler solutions later. Similarly, in T'ai-chi curing we look for the causes of disease first in lack of sleep, poor diet, lack of exercise, harmful lifestyle, etc. Only when these problems are dealt with can we look for the more complex possibilities.

It is true that you may have the flu. But taking an antibiotic is only a temporary solution. If the basic cause is not dealt with, you may get pneumonia next. If that is "cured" with penicillin, you may get a heart attack later on. All this when the underlying problem may have simply been lack of rest or excess tension. By taking drugs unnecessarily, you can interfere with the biochemical mechanisms of the body. Drugs can alter your feelings and cause you to be unknown to yourself. The chemicals alter a whole series of relationships of body mechanisms so that the biofeedback system is confused. This renders you susceptible to further illness.

A very noninvasive method of curing is by means of breath. Proper breathing allows the healing energies of the earth to flow through your body. There are breathing techniques which rebalance the energy flow, strengthening the body.

I teach one of these exercises to new students before they learn anything else. That one exercise, when done daily, is worth ten classes in the Form.

In T'ai-chi our perception of curing is an ecological one. A healthy environment requires predators as well as prey. To destroy the predator would be to destroy the prey as well, for you would upset the entire ecological balance. Within our bodies are many beings: microorganisms, organs, cells, molecules and power animals (energy patterns). Maintaining the ecological balance of all these beings is one basis of health. Curing consists of finding the imbalance and rebalancing it. Living an ecological life is the other basis of good health, and curing must take this into consideration as well. It takes more than a visit to the doctor's office and a prescription for valium to cure in this manner. But what is your health worth to you?

It is in vogue today to cure even mental illness with drugs. While there are certainly some biochemical causes of mental illness, much of it is a disease of definition, caused by our society's perception of "proper" behavior. A nonfunctioning mental patient is too often only a person with a behavior pattern that doesn't make sense within our rigid norms. It is part of almost every other society to have visions, and they are taken quite seriously by the members of those societies. But if people have visions in our society, they are not looked on so generously.

In many cultures, people practice several personality patterns, but in ours, such people are labeled with negative titles. How many visionaries are wasting their lives in mental hospitals, convinced they are sick? Those with political visions often waste their lives in jail. Perhaps the pills are going to the wrong patients. If we could give one gigantic pill to our culture, it might prove to be very powerful medicine for us all. Or perhaps we should deal with the other end first. If we gave our culture a giant enema, we might be able to unblock the free flow of creativity and feelings and live much more fulfilling lives.

Each of us can do this on a personal level by creating our own culture which we can share with friends. If each person lives a natural lifestyle, then that will soon become the prevailing culture. We have great power on an individual level to cure ourselves and to create a healing atmosphere for our families, friends and community. Do not doubt your power. That is the first step in becoming a Taoist magician and healer.

CHAPTER 6
THE EVOLUTION OF THE HUMAN MIND

A small tribe of stone-age people, the Tasaday, living in the midst of the Philippine jungle, gave scientists clues to our own evolution from this stage of culture. The tribe had been isolated from outside influences for probably over eight hundred years. The Tasaday were told that if there was anything they wanted, it would be provided for them. All they had to do was ask. But they insisted that they didn't want anything besides the metal knives the anthropologists had already given them. Puzzled, the scientists left a tape recorder in their cave and told the Tasaday that if they thought of anything they wanted, they could speak to the box and that would help the scientists understand their needs. The conversations retrieved from the tape recorder not only shed light on the Tasaday but on our own origins as well. Those conversations went something like this:

"How can we ask for things when we don't know what things there are? We know only our stream, the cave, the trees, the foods we eat and now the metal knives. Aside from these, we know of nothing else."

Tens of thousands of years ago, all humanity was in the same predicament. Who could have dreamed of all the things we have today?

Structuring the Human Mind

Yet, there were people back then, visionaries if you will, who understood that the key to achieving the great things they wished for (freedom from hunger, disease, attack, etc.) lay in the structuring of the human mind. The mind was the greatest tool at their disposal for improving their lives. From a comparative study of ancient traditions, some of which still survive today, it now seems that in all areas the same basic structure of the mind was used. Whether American Indian, Chinese, Egyptian, etc., the basic model of the universe was fairly consistent.

This may represent one of three things. First, there may have been a universal culture influencing the far reaches of the globe thousands of years ago, just as today almost the entire world wears bluejeans. Due to geologic upheavals or wars, this civilization may have been demolished, leaving only its philosophy behind. Another theory is that all these cultures have simply hit upon universal truths. Perhaps their philosophies reflect the true condition of the universe. The third theory is that the structure of the world as perceived by each culture is a reflection of the universal structure of the human mind itself.

Not only is the philosophy itself fairly universal, but the methods of teaching it as well. Children (or those just beginning to study the system) are exposed to stories which familiarize them with the principles of the philosophy they will learn later on. The philosophy itself is a multi-level system in which the real meaning is disguised. As the student progresses through the stages of learning, he is taught deeper and deeper meanings of the words he reads or hears.

This is why it is useless to try to interpret ancient texts without an understanding of the deeper meanings of the system in question. In the previous chapter, a Taoist sexual yoga was described which interprets ancient alchemical texts on the mixing of cinnabar and lead to produce an elixir of immortality as actually referring to abstinence form orgasm to achieve the same result. Controversies always surround the true meanings of these ancient texts. If they could be accurately understood, they would provide incredible clues to the evolution of the human mind as an intellectual tool. This might help solve such difficult modern problems as war and poverty.

My interpretation of the mixing of lead and cinnabar is quite different. Lead refers to the male principle (associated with seminal fluid by Taoist alchemists) and cinnabar to the female principle. The female principle is the great void, full of limitless potential, the source of the power of creativity. The male principle is outgoing energy, form, mind. The reaching of orgasm refers to the union of these two energies. To use the power of yin (female) and yet be able to create form (yang) without dissolving that form in the union of yin and yang is the meaning of sexual alchemy. The immortality referred to deals with the maintaining of form, whether of a culture or any other human-created entity, by avoiding the natural course of growth and decay, birth and death. to achieve an immortal culture, a way of life based on harmony, is the interpretation favored by this writer.

There is a sound theoretical foundation for this teaching of personal immortality. T'ai-chi students develop a firm pattern of energy centered in the Tan-tien. This central focus of energy, the spider at the center of its web, begins to feel like a solid ball, and the energy pattern emanating from it feels like a solid network of fibers. It is as substantial in its own way as physical objects.

We can accept that physical objects can last for tremendous periods of time. Yet according to Taoist teachings, physical objects are only the surface perception of more fundamental patterns of energy. If a physical object such as a mountain lasts for centuries, it is because the underlying energy pattern has lasted for that amount of time.

We have learned that by working with our own energy pattern, we can change our actual physical well-being, bringing back youthful grace, flexibility and stamina and increasing our life span to at least a small degree. Our practice of T'ai-chi-Ch'uan, then, gives us some control over the energy which gives rise to physical matter. If we can solidify this energy so that it is not dissipated by the flow of energies surrounding it, then it is theoretically possible (within this conceptual framework) to maintain the body indefinitely.

Another interpretation of immortality is that while the body dies, the energy pattern does not, and can reform or enter a new body, retaining all its qualities within a new individual. Thus, whatever skills were gained in one lifetime will be transmitted to the next body that energy pattern inhabits. There is thus an extrachromosomal inheritance for those individuals who can develop a firm energy pattern.

For those who cannot, their energy pattern, which sustained their lives, dissolves into the general flow of energy, perhaps adding skills to the general energy pattern of the species, but not retaining enough distinctness to reenter a new individual in the same form as in the previous life.

While this energy pattern is firmed in a T'ai-chi student, it cannot be allowed to become rigid. A firm pattern is not necessarily powerful. It must maintain a sensitivity, a soft, yielding quality which will allow it to maneuver after the death of the body and reenter a new individual. Firmness is a yang quality and symbolized by lead; sensitivity is a yin quality and symbolized by cinnabar.

The survival of the human race as a whole is similar in principle to the survival of an individual energy pattern. If our physical being, including the structures we have built, is termed "yang" and our culture, ideas and institutions are termed "yin," then we can relate our species' survival to the Taoist lesson of immortality. The ability of our culture, ideas and institutions to be fluid and adjust to new circumstances is as essential to our survival as the maintenance of our physical well-being. Scientific advances are one example of this fluidity. Discoveries in genetic engineering and computer technology, for example, are creating new industries and new sources of wealth, more from innovative ideas than from actual resources.

The other method of gaining wealth and power is to conquer countries which are weak militarily but rich in resources, whether minerals or cheap labor. This is similar in principle to those male Taoists who, rather than developing the yin quality within themselves, attempt to rob this quality from women through the method of sexual yoga previously described. In this manner, they hope to achieve personal immortality.

My objections to Taoist yoga are therefore not based on a disbelief in the principles underlying the teachings of immortality, but in their application. By analyzing these teachings and their symbolic implications, I hope to convey a feeling for the connections between how we live our lives as individuals and the actions and quality of our society as a whole.

Cultural Anthropology

To understand the deeper meanings of ancient teachings, I place my faith in a comparative study of surviving ancient cultures. I have been directly involved in T'ai-chi and have also been apprenticed to teachers of Egyptian, Hebrew and Celtic mysticism. I have also studied other cultures on an intellectual level, and while this study will take the rest of my life to even scratch the surface, I feel that a description of my observations gained up to this point is essential to a more complete understanding of T'ai-chi. Not only will such a discussion place T'ai-chi in a wider context, but a comparison of other cultures' techniques for achieving similar goals will make the techniques of T'ai-chi far more comprehensible and usable in your everyday life.

The teaching device of hiding the true meaning of the teaching from the student until he is ready to absorb it (hermetics), works on an evolutionary level as well. A teacher of many people must be sensitive to the level of understanding of the people in his culture. His truths must be couched in simpler terms than he himself comprehends. Each teacher hopes that his contribution will advance the overall wisdom of his people so that the next generation may perceive the next level of "truth."

In the book *The Tribe That Hides from Man*, the Villas-Boas brothers were faced with the task of preparing several South American Indian tirbes for the onslaught of the Brazilian government's attempt to open the interior to "exploitation." At that time, according to Adrian Cowell, the author, each tribe considered members of other tribes fair game. Just as they hunted animals for food, they would hunt other Indians for their possessions (or women). Even within a tribe, there were frequent murders. (Luckily, we civilized people are far more advanced.)

The brothers first tried to end the intratribal killings, arguing that since the other tribes frequently attacked them, they needed all the manpower they could muster. Each murder made them weaker as a tribe. Then they told all the tribes that the Europeans were their common enemy and that they should stop the intertribal killings to prepare for the onslaught of the Brazilians. This of course enraged the Brazilians, but the third step in this plan was to give the Indians the standard argument, "All people are brothers, so we shouldn't kill anyone." (The problem has since been partially solved, as there are now very few Indians left to talk to.)

This same step-by-step approach to developing a new consciousness has taken place many times in history. Of course, the level of warfare and murder in modern times suggests that the attempt has not succeeded. And yet, can we ever stop trying? Surely many writers, this one included, like to feel that they are part of the attempt.

Rites of Passage

When an individual student progresses up the various levels of understanding, this process is often referred to as "rites of passage." Frequently, a child's rite of passage is based on the concept of taking responsibility for his life and his tribe. The child is no longer to be pampered, but must now bear his share of the load. These rites are often associated with trials of pain, deprivation and endurance (in the case of males) to "toughen" the child. In this way, he has a frame of reference for suffering, so that his burdens in taking care of his people will seem mild by comparison. The prospect of suffering will no longer prevent him from carrying out his duties.

There is a body of belief today that the entire earth is about to undergo a rite of passage. According to this theory, a major geologic upheaval is soon to hit us (around the mid to late 1980s) and only those who are spiritual enough, tough enough, or possess certain other qualities will be able to survive.

Certainly the threat of nuclear war, habitat destruction and chemical poisoning is enough to at least partially justify this idea, although I don't know if being spiritual will help those who drink polluted water (except that they may become aware enough to drink purified water). But I do believe that the concept of linking rites of passage and the growth of awareness in individuals to that of our entire civilization is a powerful perspective by which to achieve a better world.

World View

If we can understand the roots of our present world view and its evolution up to our present time, perhaps we can gain an insight into the future and the role of T'ai-chi in that future.

I hope I will not be ridiculed for the meagerness of my own wisdom in this chapter. But if I can make this confusing world a bit more comprehensible for even a few people, this chapter and the entire book will have been worth writing.

It is difficult to accept that the world we view is, to a great extent, a product of the way in which we look at it. Yet, several people, witnessing an accident or some other event, will commonly report differing accounts of that event. The courts are filled with people offering different perspectives of a single situation. I have often discussed a book with another person who had read the same book, only to find that his recollection was quite different from mine.

There is the story of a visitor to a Zen monastery. The abbot suggested that the visitor hold a Zen conversation with one of the monks of the monastery. Such conversations are designed to show one's awareness of Zen and seem quite incomprehensible to those not familiar with this teaching method. The monk, a man who had lost a finger in an accident, and the visitor sat down for their Zen discussion. The visitor raised one finger. The monk raised two. The visitor countered with three and the monk with four. The visitor then raised all five fingers and the monk displayed a closed fist, whereupon the visitor got up and went to the abbot.

"How did your discussion go?" asked the abbot.

"Your monk is very astute," replied the visitor. "I raised one finger to show that all things are really a product of the one universal force. He raised two fingers to show that while there is one force, this force divides into the two, yin and yang, to produce all things.

"I then countered with three fingers to show that energy, matter and the observer are all one and that their distinction is just an illusion. Masterfully, your monk raised four fingers to point out the four directions and the four basic elements, which are more fundamental than the distinction I had raised.

"My only hope was to raise five fingers, to point out to him that he had forgotten the fifth element of consciousness itself, which unifies the others. When he showed me a closed fist, to explain the unity of consciousness with that of which it is conscious, I knew I had lost the discussion and left. Your monk is of a much higher level of awareness than I."

Later that day, the abbot asked the monk his impression of the discussion.

"The rude fellow raised a finger to point out that I had lost one of my fingers. I raised two fingers to let him know that if he did not mind his manners, I would poke both his eyes out. He then raised three fingers to show that of my four extremities, only three were complete. At that point, I was ready to jump the fellow, but I raised four fingers to warn him that if he did not guard his manners, I would break all four of his extremities. Then the fellow raised five fingers to show me that his hand was intact. I raised my fist and was about to punch him when he ran out of the room."

Each society has its tales of how the world came into being and how the world works. Generally the people within a society believe these tales, for they have been exposed to them since childhood. Furthermore, the structure of that society is based on their understanding, again reinforcing that structure in the minds of its citizens.

Our own society is no exception. We accept many beliefs blindly, some of which this book has attempted to challenge. We accept the separation of waking from dreaming states, conscious from subconscious, self from other and the inferiority of certain races as natural. The mad rush to produce, the germ theory of disease, etc., is as accepted here as conflicting ideas in other cultures are accepted by their people. These beliefs are not innocuous, but affect the quality of life of individuals and the survival of all of us. Our pollution of the environment, our failure to maintain our health, etc., have been cited previously as examples. But on a more personal level, a failure to understand and utilize your world view can have disastrous effects.

Using World View to Empower Your Life

While a full discussion of the role of T'ai-chi-Ch'uan in interpersonal relations must wait for Volume II, let me use one example here. The Long Island School of T'ai-chi-Ch'uan provides individual counseling from a Taoist perspective. The following is an example of a discussion I might have with a client to enable him to gain power over his life. The problem in question is a fear of approaching women.

"You must build yourself a temple of power. This is actually a structure of energy rather than a physical structure. One of the ways to obtain the building blocks for this temple of power is by exchanging energy with another person. This energy must be freely given. Just as a physical temple needs doors, bricks, windows, floors, etc., you need many parts for your energy temple and some must be obtained from other people.

"Wait for a woman to give you a gift of energy. You will know when someone has done this because you will feel a warm feeling within you about that person. When this has happened, you must return something of equal value. Go up to that person and give her a warm feeling. Tell her that you just noticed something about her that made you feel good and that you thought she would like to know. If she seems interested in continuing the conversation, so much the better. But if not, you have accomplished your main goal—giving her back a gift of energy.

"If you fail to return the gift, her BM will yank it back. Even if she (her mind) responds to you in a negative way when you talk to her, this is of no consequence. Her BM gave you the gift of energy and you gave her BM a gift in return. The transaction has been completed. You have added another energy-brick to your temple of power.

"When that temple is strong enough, you will be able to connect with the woman you need. Furthermore, these energy transactions help others to build their temples, so you will have done good deeds for others."

This description of a male-female first-time interaction is certainly different from what most of us are used to. It is based on a different world view. The manner in which the client deals with first-time meetings with women will be changed, as will the feelings within him. This perspective is not a trick one uses to gain courage to say hello. It's not a "line" to open a conversation. It's a method of switching to an alternate world view—one that gives you more power in life. It's a different way of explaining what is going on in the world. If you use it and it works, you will become convinced of its validity.

 It may be said without exaggeration that what we see in our environment is a result of what we look for. Our world view tells us what we should pay attention to. A politician looks for votes and communists, an angry person seeks conflicts, a starving person seeks food. In this manner, our world view affects, to a great extent, how we live our lives, how we view ourselves and how much power we have as individuals. The above client would have gained little power in life if he had been convinced that changing his brand of deodorant was the key to meeting women. To blindly accept the prevailing world view is equivalent to accepting any drug you are offered, as described in the previous chapter.

Changing Your World View

How do you develop the freedom to change your world view when you have been thoroughly programmed with the prevailing world view? Your very personality, your hopes and dreams in life and the entire structure of your knowledge are based on a single world view. When you've invested your whole life in something, you're not likely to give it up unless forced to do so or unless convinced that your life and well-being depend on it.

Once you have been convinced, you need tools with which to make the change. One such tool is T'ai-chi-Ch'uan. Another is the study of an alternate world view. By studying a different perspective and understanding its usefulness, you can loosen your grip on your old world view and not regard the alternate world view as primitive.

This chapter consists largely of a description of the Western mystical world view and the comparison of its methods and goals with those of T'ai-chi-Ch'uan. After reading this chapter and having these two new world views under your belt, you should be able to see your world in a more flexible light. Perhaps the world isn't exactly as you think you see it. In addition, by studying these new world views, it will be easier to understand the use of the mind as a tool with which we create our world. By learning about the roots and growth of the mind, we may be able to gain creative control of our world view as a society and improve it so as to eliminate the monumental problems which now face us. We will be performing a mid-course maneuver, so to speak, in our mental evolution, similar to the way a satellite's trajectory is altered if it goes off course.

Western Mysticism

Let us then examine the roots of modern science, the roots of our world view— Western mysticism. By comparing the Eastern system of T'ai-chi-Ch'uan to what is loosely termed Western mysticism (actually an amalgamation of systems from the ancient Middle East, Mediterranean and Europe), we will gain a greater insight into the place of T'ai-chi-Ch'uan in the world-wide evolution of the human mind. Most of the ancient world views are similar, whether American Indian, Taoist, Buddhist, Egyptian or Hebrew. By studying Western mysticism, we will be learning the basic principles common to all these teachings.

Most of us have had no choice in our world view. We have adopted the knowledge available from our parents, our schools and the streets. A student of Western mysticism will build his alternate world view himself. He will study how to create a new perspective so vivid that he will convincingly see the world in its own terms. By doing so, he will gradually understand the way in which world views in general are programmed into people and how the prevailing world view of his culture was programmed into his own mind. But with the alternate world view, there is a difference. Since he consciously programmed it into himself, he retains control over it. He is not a slave to that perspective, but can "switch" into it with an act of his will. Once he has two world views at his disposal, he can see vividly that much of the world he took to be absolute, objective truth is, in reality, a subjective perspective.

The Elements

The student will begin his study of Western mysticism by learning "the elements." The elements are powers or forces which have created the world as we know it. There are four (or five, counting spirit or consciousness). Various names are given to each of these four powers, depending on the sect of Western mysticism. Let us call them Earth, Air, Fire and Water. The powers themselves are not dirt, oxygen, nitrogen, etc.; these are merely the names given to examples of each of the four powers. Since there are four basic forces in the universe, according to this world view, each subject area of our lives has four aspects. The student learns to associate each area of his life with one of these aspects.

The human mind is organized on the basis of association centers. If I pick the subject of ice cream, for example, the words, "taste," "cold," "food," "dessert," "melt," etc., are associated with the central word, "ice cream." Our thinking minds are a network of such subject associations. Our world view can be defined as a particular association structure which gives us our understanding of how everything is related to everything else.

By creating four basic association centers, Earth, Air, Fire and Water, and learning a method of associating all things with them, you are creating a new association structure. You are taking creative control over your own mind. Let us do that now.

1. *Air: Mind, Space, Hearing, Spring, East*

Air is space, within which the eagle soars. Floating over miles of wilderness, it can swoop down at any moment to capture a tiny mouse. Air is mind, imagination, communication, new beginnings.

With the mind, you can soar to the outer reaches of space or zero in on a tiny topic, dissecting it mercilessly until it has been ripped to pieces. You begin a new project with a new idea. Then it takes will, desire and method to go through with it. Mind is like spring, new ideas beginning new endeavors, as the plants waken and begin to grow. A new idea may even start a new culture, business or invention. According to legend, when God breathed the breath of life into Adam, human life began. When you see something new and startling, you gasp in surprise.

Air is associated with curiosity, which causes you to take the first step. It is freedom, forward movement. Because of this, it is considered a "male" (yang) energy. This doesn't mean that women don't possess the qualities of Air; it is, unfortunately, merely a chauvinistic term. The terms yin and yang (although not part of Western vocabulary) are better terms, and I will use them from now on.

The sun rises in the east, starting a new day, and so Air is east. It is likewise the element of dawn. An overabundance of Air produces boasting (hot Air) as well as frivolousness. The second quality comes about when too much is said about a subject until you are just talking for the sake of talking and not really saying anything. Too much Air can produce knowledge without wisdom (the wisdom of experience). True understanding consists of more than facts alone. A balance of the elements is essential for wisdom.

Air in the form of a tornado, which spins around at a great speed, is as destructive as a mind that spins around disconnected from the world. When two great wind currents intersect, a swirling tornado may result. A mind faced with two opposing sets of values or perspectives may suffer the same result, injuring the person to whom it belongs.

A gentle breeze is like a simple, potent statement. You drop what you are doing to feel the breeze and to notice if it brings scents or sounds from the distance. A gentle suggestion will be listened to much sooner than a browbeating harangue. The simple lyric of a song may carry with it implications of meaning which are the harbinger of a new perspective.

Air is the fresh breath you take in the chill of the morning. It is the optimism of a new day, a new way. While Air is the free, inspired mind, Fire is used to represent logic.

2. *Fire: Will, Energy, Seeing, Summer, South*

Fire is many things. It is energy and heat. Used to cook food, it is a symbol of purification. "Trial by Fire" refers to learning through hard experience. It is the purification of the soul, the basis of many rites of passage.

For tens of thousands of years, our species has used Fire as protection against wild animals, and this has established it as a symbol of protection. But it is a two-edged sword, for while Fire protects, it can also destroy.

As a campfire, surrounded by the tribe, it is the center of the circle, the source of warmth and protection. It is a magical symbol, and many, if not most magic rituals are conducted in a "magic circle" with a candle or Fire at the center.

As a smelter of metallic ores, Fire is the symbol of crafts and skills of every kind and generally the symbol of craft knowledge. "Light" is often used to signify knowledge or spiritual illumination. While Air represents the mind's ability to soar, Fire represents the mental data itself.* By transforming raw ores into metals and several metals into alloys, it is the symbol of transformation on a personal level as well. The transformation into a spiritual being is pictured as a trial by Fire to reach the source of Light (God, BM, Tao, etc.).

Fire is the south, the summer, season of the most intense sun. It is growth and power. The burning sun's rays fall upon the earth, causing all life to grow and flourish. Fire is the symbol of will, the ability to focus your energy on a project or magical endeavor. The ability to sustain your will over a long period of time will insure the success of your work. As the sun's energy is stored in plants, to be harvested in the fall and used, your sustained will in learning is

*Although in some branches of Western mysticism, Air represents logical thinking, while Fire represents inspriational knowledge.

harvested when you finally begin to work as an adult and make use of your skills. The will is stored within the BM in the form of skill to be "harvested" whenever needed. Your increasing amounts of skill is an energy storage in the sense that the same work requries less effort as you gain skill at it.

3. *Water: Emotion, Time, Taste, Autumn, West*

Water flows around obstacles and conforms to the container that holds it. It does not resist the rocks in a stream but flows by effortlessly, without loss of forward momentum. It is the universal solvent, allowing various chemicals to mix and combine. Within Water, these chemicals come to a natural harmony and, in their various combinations, form new compounds.

Water as emotion allows people to express their feelings, make compromises and live in harmony. The relationships among people form new families and institutions. As poisonous chemicals may seep unseen into a clean lake, negative emotions can seep into you without your realizing it. The emotional state of a person may be very calm, like a calm lake, yet when the winds of the mind sweep across it, the surface is disturbed by waves. Then it becomes difficult to see through to the bottom of the lake, for the mud below has been churned up. When your mind churns up your emotions, you lose sight of your true self and your true feelings.

As with all the elements, a preponderance of Water, not balanced with the other elements, can cause damage. A tidal wave can destroy a city. Unbalanced emotions can destroy a person's life. Yet, we cannot survive without Water. A drought can destroy an entire country's crops, causing mass starvation. Too much Fire (the sun) can destroy crops as easily as too much Water (a flood). The elements must be balanced in order to be effective.

In your life too much emotion in the form of a desire to play music, say, must be balanced with the will and energy to spend many hours learning the notes and scales. Too much Water can douse the Fire. Wild emotional swings can wear out your will to the point where you give up your practice. If there is a great deal of will, if you are pushing yourself to do something but there is little desire to do it, you won't get far. This is a case of too much Fire and too little Water.

Water also represents time, which is said to flow like a river. Our concept of time as something which moves in a straight line at a steady pace (historical time) has its roots in ancient philosophy, as shown by representing time as a flowing river. When you feel enthusiastic, time seems to flow quickly. When life is boring, the day drags. This is subjective time.

Water has the ability to merge. A single drop can merge with an ocean to become part of the ocean. Unless that drop of Water is in a container, it is indistinguishable from the rest of the ocean. When you fall in love, you can also lose your individual identity. If you become part of an emotional mob scene, the same is true.

The ability to retain your individuality is represented by Earth, the next element on our list. Too much Earth would encase you in a shell from which you would never emerge. Again, it is the balance of individuality and the ability to merge which is essential, Earth balanced with Water.

Let us now mix Water, Earth and Fire. Fire and Water produce steam. Earth (as a ceramic container in the form of a tube) can channel that steam to a generator to perform useful work. If you can learn to balance your will and emotions (as in the case of playing an instrument), then you must channel them into a particular direction. That is, you participate in a structured teaching such as music or T'ai-chi-Ch'uan, which will channel your energy and desire for your benefit.

Let's bring Air back into the picture. Air (in the form of steam) is what actually hits the generator, creating a useful form of power. It conveys the power which was contained in the Fire to the blades of the generator to produce electricity.

The music teacher conveys his knowledge to the student via words and ideas. The power of the teacher's will (Fire) is conveyed by ideas and imagery. Musical notation is a form of imagery that conveys the will of the composer. The student's will is conveyed to his fingers via imagery. He may imagine the music as musical notation, colors, etc. In T'ai-chi-Ch'uan, you imagine a tiger and somehow your body becomes tiger-like in its movements. In this manner, teachings about how to live your life are conveyed by use of the elements.

4. *Earth: Body, Matter, Touch, Winter, North*

Earth is immediate and tangible. It is the hard, physical reality of our everyday lives. You may hit on a new idea, have the will to carry it out and be excited about it emotionally, but at some point, you must get down into the dirt and actually *do* it. Earth is "doing."

It is form, the earthenware cup which can hold Water, Air and even Fire. Earth gives form to the other three elements. It is the house which sets apart a certain area as your own. Earth provides distinctions between things and controls the proportions of each ingredient.

As an aqueduct, it channels Water to bring it to the town. As your body, it is the apparent container of your individuality. Earth is ego and self-protection. Your body is the crucible in which magical elixirs are brewed. Earth is a medium which allows seeds to grow, provided the proper amount of Air, warmth (Fire) and moisture (Water) are present also.

Earth is the surface upon which your life takes place. The physical world itself is only the surface of a much deeper universe. Your senses and your world view perceive in terms of physical matter, yet there is much beyond your senses and your world view. Earth itself is a world view, for it structures, gives form to the world you perceive. A preponderance of Earth ties you down to a single world view, causing stubborness and narrow-mindedness. The cure for this problem is Air, for Air allows you to soar high and realize that your world view is but one small area of a vast world. The medicine of Air can be given in the form of a vacation, movement away from the old grind, or reading exciting fiction to soar away from your tiny little corner of the world.

Too much Earth can also cause lethargy, just as a rock remains immobile. A cure for this problem is Fire, an outgoing, yang energy. (Earth and Water are yin.) Sometimes it takes a concerted effort of will to get out of a rut. You may not be excited about getting moving, but if you just do it, the excitement will be generated along with the movement. It often takes an act of will to get up in the morning, but once up, the excitement of the day soon hits you.

The silence of Earth is conducive to inner awareness. The Old Testament contains the words, "Be still and know that I am God." Moses "met" God on Mount Sinai, certainly a very large rock. Mountains represent stability and Earth is a stable element. It grounds and holds. It is the element of gravity, magnetism and physical attraction. A flood eventually subsides when the excess Water has been absorbed into the Earth. The grounding of Earth is good for an excess of Water (emotion).

An Earth person faced with a person experiencing excess Water or Fire will go over and give him or her a hug, absorbing the Water or the heat of the Fire. He has a large capacity to absorb the energy and emotions of others, calming them down.

Earth is inertia, providing a steady connection to your home while traveling and a connection to your inner peace when faced with turmoil. The roots of trees grow into the earth to hold them fast, as your attention grows into your world view to hold you to this world.

The Magical Self

Magic is the same system used in T'ai-chi, except that the elements are Wood, Fire, Earth, Metal and Water. The beginner's lessons consist largely in learning the qualities of theses elements on a personality level and how they interact. The combining of elements is called "alchemy" and was responsible, in the Middle East and North Africa, for the development of the science of chemistry and scientific methodology in general. The beginning student of alchemy learned to combine actual chemical elements over a flame. This was a physical representation of the true purpose of alchemy—the creation of a spiritual being within oneself. Alchemy was a symbolic teaching device for spiritual growth. Turning lead into gold, the ultimate goal of alchemy, really meant turning a blubbering dolt of a beginning student into a mature adult.

Our modern science owes much of its origin to alchemy, but today the personal development aspect has been abandoned. Modern science has satisfied itself with remaining at the level of the beginning student and shows no interest in the true teachings of alchemy. Alchemists are ridiculed for trying to turn lead into gold, while modern scientists do not even know what that process really means.

The abandonment of personal development has led to the destructive application of modern science. Yet many of the world's greatest scientists, as individuals, were very spiritual people. A large number of them were involved in or headed Western mystical orders. Pythagoras and Benjamin Franklin were but two notable examples.

The process of mixing the elements in proper proportion is known as developing a "magical self." This special personality is molded by each magician, as is his world view. In fact, the magical personality is designed to operate within the magical world view, as our personality has been molded to operate within our present world view. This work of using and mixing the elements is done through magical ritual.

Ritual

A ritual is a physical representation of the principles of the alternate world view. Alchemy is a ritual in the sense that it involves precise physical movements of certain objects which represent deeper meanings.

The more common form of ritual takes place around an altar, a central table upon which rest several objects. The tabletop represents our world and our lives and the area surrounding it represents the greater universe of which we are only dimly aware. Certain objects represent each of the four elements: a bowl of water for Water, a bowl of salt for Earth, a burning charcoal for Fire and incense placed on the charcoal for Air. Candles are used to represent the greater energies, the Goddess and the God (yin and yang).

The first step in the ritual is to create a magical circle around the area to separate the sacred world from the profane world. This is done by walking around the altar or by merely imagining a circle. Some magicians "draw" a circle on the ground with a sword.

A High Priestess and High Priest conduct the ritual unless it is a solitary ritual, as is usual for magical work. Group rituals are performed only once in awhile, as most people have other commitments, such as earning a living, and cannot meet very often.

The next step in elemental ritual is to invoke or call down the elemental forces, making sure to invoke each in the compass direction which represents it. Within the ritual itself, the various objects are manipulated in such a way as to represent the inner dynamics of the world view they are teaching. Poetry and prose are spoken, denoting the meaning of each movement. Even the bodies of the High Priestess and High Priest are magical power objects, for they call down the corresponding yin or yang force to speak to the group through their bodies.

In higher-level magical rituals, a whole heirarchy of spirits and forces may be called upon to perform various tasks at the magician's request. Some of these forces are visualizations of the various elements within the magician and others are visualizations of the forces of nature. Not all such forces or beings are benevolent, so the magician must exercise strict control over them and not allow them to possess him.

Perhaps the most confusing and abhorrent ritual known to the average person is that of human sacrifice, such as among the Aztecs of Central America. (This is *not* a ritual practiced by Western mystics!) In this gory practice, people from neighboring tribes had their still-throbbing hearts cut out, held up to the sun and then thrown into a huge stone bowl. This has usually been interpreted as a sacrifice to the Aztec god and left at that. But let's take a closer look at the symbolism.

The sun is generally a symbol of the thinking mind (not of creative thought, as is Air). The heart is a universal symbol of the feeling and intuitive part of ourselves (BM). This ritual, then, was a symbolic sacrifice of the BM to the thinking mind. Such a sacrifice occurs in all city-state societies. If each person was connected to his creative center, the population would be difficult to subdue and control. The sacrifice of BM to mind is part of our own culture as well, but we don't announce it in such an obvious way. In the case of the Aztecs, the victims were prisoners of war forced to their horrible fate by soldiers. It was a priest who held the knife and slit open their chests.

In your case the knife is held by your own programming, your own fears, as in the Zen story of the master holding a stick over the head of his students in Chapter Five. If you can muster the courage to grab that knife and toss it away, you will be freed to live your life with your heart intact.

This is the purpose of magical ritual in Western mysticism. If your life is filled with the storms of Air (mind) and the flames of Fire (thought, a demanding temperament), both of which are yang energies, you must counterbalance them with yin energies. Water will restore feeling and intuition, while Earth will restore calm and attention to practical matters. True magical ritual is a way to keep your life in balance. Once balanced, you can grow as a person and experience all life has to offer. You can develop your powers as a human being to the fullest.

As the student progresses, he is taught many rituals, each representing a change in consciousness. This allows him to practice "shape-shifting," that is, changing the shape of his consciousness. Among American Indians, the equivalent would be working with power animals. Each power animal represents an energy which performs a rebalancing function and is used in healing. Each power animal is a summation of the quality of personality, energy flow, etc., of that energy pattern. By learning to become aware of various patterns of energy, you acquire the abilities and powers of those power animals. Each power animal is known to bring with it certain powers. Once you have acquired a power animal, you must exercise it in order to keep it, just as the various Forms in T'ai-chi-Ch'uan must be constantly practiced. A medicine person (shaman) will sink beneath the earth to find the proper power animal to bring to his patient. Sickness is diagnosed as the lack of a power animal or the loss of one obtained previously.

Whether the shape-shifting of Western mysticism, the energy patterns of T'ai-chi-Ch'uan or the power animals of shamans, it is all the same practice; only the names have been changed to confuse the innocent.

The Qabala

The Qabala is the basic model of the Western mystical world view, composed of ten circles called Sephiroth, arranged in three vertical rows. The left row, or "pillar," represents severity, or yang. The right pillar represents mercy, or yin. The central pillar represents the middle path, or the balance between yin and yang. Furthermore, each Sephiroth represents a different stage, or aspect, of consciousness. Lines drawn from one Sephiroth to another represent the process of changes in consciousness. From the uppermost central Sephiroth of Kether (Tao), or pure, undifferentiated energy, to the lower Sephiroth of Malkuth, or physical matter, we create the world around us through various processes of consciousness.

The Qabala is known as the Tree of Life and is a secret, "mouth-to-ear" teaching of the Hebrews. This teaching may have been originally Egyptian and is one reason for the Hebrews to consider themselves the "chosen people of God," for it was they who carried on this teaching after the decline of Egypt. But the Egyptians may not have been the originators of the Qabala: there are stories of much more ancient civilizations which developed world-wide dominance, such as Atlantis and Mu. These civilizations, according to legend, were destroyed by geologic upheaval, as our own civilization is supposed to be in a few short years. (So live it up, while there's still baseball and hot dogs.)

The Qabala is also based on mathematics: a number is assigned to each word in the language (each letter being represented by a number). The Old Testament is said by Hebrew scholars to be written with this in mind, the numerical values of each word and sentence revealing hidden meanings. This is the basis for the mystical science of numerology. The universe is envisaged as a complex structure of mathematics, obviously, a predominately mental perspective. In fact, some might interpret the Qabala as implying that thought is more spiritual than the physical world because it is closer to Kether (primordial Tao). To me, a student of the Qabala should be required to open and develop all Sephiroth, all aspects of consciousness. His development should not be thought of as stepping from one Sephiroth to another, but rather engaging all of them in his life.

Just as the T'ai-chi student studies the implications of each quality of the Form in living his life, the Qabala student studies each Sephiroth and its implications. While the Sephiroth are given such names as Wisdom, Understanding, Beauty, Victory, etc., these names are merely labels, as Air and Water are labels for two of the elements. The Qabala student learns to use each Sephiroth as a focusing point for his attention, through which he opens himself up to the energies of nature.

Tarot

The Tarot is a deck of seventy-eight cards, each with a different drawing representing a certain aspect of the Western mystical teaching. They are arranged in two sets. One is a set of twenty-two, called the "major arcana." These represent the twenty-two "paths" from one Sephiroth to another, according to the diagram of the Tree of Life. They may be understood as steps in the raising of consciousness the student must take to develop into a fully mature being.

The second set, consisting of fifty-six cards, is divided into four suits: Wands, Cups, Swords and Pentacles (representing Air, Water, Fire and Earth). Each suit contains fourteen cards. The cards are visual representations of the underlying teachings. The Two of Swords, for example, depicts a young woman sitting on a stone bench before a large body of water, out of which protrude large rocks. She is blindfolded, facing away from the water, and holds in her crossed hands two swords pointing to the upper corners of the card. A crescent moon can be seen in the background.

In one interpretation of this card, the woman is blind (blindfold) to the emotional (Water) consequences of her decision-making (the two crossed swords denoting a decision one way or the other). She sits on a stone bench (stone is a symbol of an emotionless attitude as well as of the stability which seems to come from repressing feelings). In the water, the rocks show the bumpy path you must take when you are willing to feel, for opening yourself up to feelings can bring sadness as well as joy. The moon, a symbol of higher wisdom and the yin force of intuition and feeling, hangs over the water.

In this manner, the student of Tarot can learn many lessons from the cards. Each card deserves a separate chapter; their implications are almost endless. The particular interpretation you get from each card is a matter of intuition, of your psychic sense. If you are troubled, you can stare at a card until your own subconscious begins to use the symbolism in the card to speak to you. Sudden insights as to the meaning of the card will reach your consciousness from your subconscious. Your BM will be trying to communicate with you.

When you use the Tarot, you shuffle the cards, then place several down on a table, face up, in a prearranged pattern. The relationships of the positions of the cards have added significance. Each position represents an aspect of your life, such as how you see your present situation, your fears, the lesson you will have to learn, the programming within you which is affecting the situation, etc. The cards are usually read to clarify a particular situation for someone else. It's hard to do a reading for yourself.

I used to do several readings a week for people, using both Western mystical and T'ai-chi interpretations of the cards. I was constantly amazed at the accuracy of my readings, even though I insisted the person not tell me anything about his situation until after the reading.

How do they work? There are several explanations. They may just represent universal qualities we all try to deal with in our lives. But the cards are too accurate too often for that. Perhaps the cards which are picked for the reading magically fall into the right places on the table. I don't have the answer, but as long as they work and are useful, I will use them.

Besides this personal counseling aspect of Tarot, there is another benefit. Tarot develops holographic attention. Within each card are several symbols. Their arrangement on the cards builds a complex story, as I have just shown. Placing several such "stories" on the table in a particular pattern builds a larger story.

The complex web of interrelationships of the symbols and cards must be perceived as a whole in order to read the larger story. It is a nonlinear mode of communication and probably a carry-over from original methods of written communication. Drawings and diagrams found in unearthed ancient cities are almost certainly more than mere decorations. Even a short involvement with mystical teachings will convince anyone that people involved in such energy perspectives were not haphazard or flip in their drawings. Such drawings are often handed down through generations, as is still done today among many tribal peoples. A study of such drawings by people properly trained in the energy perspective would shed light on the world views of these ancient people.

Tarot is a highly sophisticated version of such ancient drawings, and its history, like that of the Qabala, is not clearly known. It has been used as a fortune-telling game, and those who go for readings usually want to know when they will meet that tall, dark, handsome stranger. But this is not what Tarot was designed for.

I use it to display, in pictorial and symbolic form, the energy pattern of a particular person at a particular time. The cards show how a person perceives his world and how he reacts to it. In this manner, they can show his future, for we create our own futures by the way we deal with situations as they come up. By understanding how he creates his own world in this manner, the person for whom I read can alter his approach and thus alter his future.

As far as predicting the future is concerned, Tarot is designed to enable you to create your own future by taking creative control of your inner being, your personality. When a reader "predicts your future," he must assume that you will not change or learn anything of value from the cards. Only if you continue to interact with your environment in the same old way can your future be predicted accurately.

Let's take a look at one more card, the Page of Cups. A young man stands on the ground before a large body of water. The waves seem to indicate that these are troubled waters. He wears fine clothes and in his right hand holds a cup which contains a single fish which is half in, half out of the cup. The fish faces the Page.

A fish, symbol of individual feelings, belongs in the water, symbol of our emotional aspect. The Page's emotions are in turmoil, so he tries to single them out in order to find out what's wrong. But by caging the fish in a cup (symbol of Water), he has interrupted the free flow of feelings (the swimming of the fish) and has not succeeded in calming himself. The fish, water, hat and part of the Page's costume are blue, the color of healing and peacefulness. When the fish is allowed to return to the ocean, the mind (hat) and body (costume) of the Page will once again be in harmony. The extremities of the Page, including the arm which holds the cup, are clothed in red. Red is a symbol of energy and passion. It is his unbalanced passion which has created his emotional turmoil.*

---

*The cards described are from the Rider-Waite Tarot deck.

Astrology

There are several principles common among most ancient civilizations. One of these is "as above, so below." The natural principles and rhythms governing the movements of stars and planets within the galaxy are the same principles governing smaller processes such as the activity of cells within the body. The principles of nature governing the physical world are the same as those governing the emotional and mental worlds.

This belief gained reinforcement with the discovery that the celestial bodies moved about the sky in precise patterns which could be mapped out mathematically. Here on earth, the seasons, the behavior of animals, the tides, cycles of flooding, etc., all proceed according to strict patterns. If any one pattern could be worked out with mathematical accuracy, then surely this would provide the key to all natural processes, thought the ancients. The Qabala is one of the results of this study. Astrology is another.

By mapping out the pattern of movements of the planets and stars, it was thought that the actual formula by which the universe works on all levels could be discovered. And thus was born the mechanistic view of the universe (the universe as a big machine), of which Newton was only one of the later exponents.

Yet, according to the mystical science of astrology, we do have free will. By understanding the universal machine, we can prepare for the fortunes and misfortunes it brings. In this way, we can gain more control over our lives.

The moment and place you were born is of great significance in astrology. Each place and time emanates "from the void" according to a certain underlying pattern of energy. Each person (that is, the BM or soul) is said to choose to be born at a certain time and place so as to gain certain experiences in life. Circumstances of birth will endow the person with the strengths and weaknesses of the corresponding energy pattern. The soul is said to pass through many lifetimes, as we pass through many wakings from sleep in our lives. When the soul grows and learns enough, it passes to another level of existence, just as a person in one lifetime passes from infancy through childhood, adolescence, middle age and old age.

By mapping out the pattern of energy of a person's birth time and place (casting his natal astrology chart), you can tell approximately what a person's life will be like. The purpose of life, according to this perspective, is to allow the inner being to grow and mature and to live in harmony with the natural cycles. An astrologer will compare your own chart with the configuration of the heavens (representing the universal pattern of energy) for the next few months or years. He will show you where and how there are conflicts between the two and how nature will reinforce your own strong points. Astrology does not emphasize actually feeling these forces of nature. It is largely a mental discipline, as is Western mysticism in general, and uses mathematics rather than body sensitivity.

Psychic Development

The branch of Western mysticism which deals with direct awareness is called psychic development. This is the development of the energy sense, as in T'ai-chi-

Ch'uan, and complements the mental, mathematical study of energy patterns. Psychics will not only sense the energy pattern of a person but can also detect energies left by people in inanimate objects. I have seen psychics move to a different chair because they claimed someone had left uncomfortable energy on the chair.

Mental influence over inanimate objects is a controversial matter. I have seen few demonstrations of this art, but let me describe one such instance. I was invited to a party of psychics. My car died jsut as I pulled into the driveway. I cleaned the battery terminals and checked for broken wires but found nothing. After turning the ignition on and off for fifteen minutes, I finally decided to join the party and worry about the car later.

Explaining my situation to the psychics, one of them went to my car, climbed in, concentrated on the ignition switch for a few seconds and turned the key. The car started and worked later on as well, all the way home. (I later found the slightly loose wire and fixed it.) Of course, it could just be "coincidence." Perhaps a wind swept by the car after I tried to start it and jostled the wire.

Central to psychic development is the opening of the chakras (energy centers along the spine). The chakras of Western mysticism correspond approximately to those of all other systems. The chakras are understood to be the points within the physical body which connect with the astral or spiritual body (to be discussed next). Through each chakra, you can be aware of an aspect of the universal energy pattern. In this way, each chakra is like a sense. By channeling energy from the ground up through the top of the head, Western mystics hope to open up and clear these spiritual centers.

The psychic art of psychometry consists of perceiving the energy of an object. A psychic can tell where the object has been and who has been around it. I once showed a rock to a well-known Long Island psychic. this rock had been in an American Indian medicine wheel ceremony several months previously. Holding the rock in her palm, this psychic not only described the entire scene but described the man who had brought me there as well. I then placed my palm on hers to show her the T'ai-chi version of the energy sense and described to her the house she had grown up in as a child.

Another aspect of the psychic art is the ability to perceive the feelings of others. Arguments between people are often caused by their inability to know their own feelings. If one of the two could see within the other and understand his or her feelings, a lot of anger could be averted. The psychic energy sense is one which is available to all with a little training. Every culture has its method of cultivating it.

The Astral Body

The astral body may be thought of as that part of the energy pattern which condenses to form the physical body. It is partway in composition between physical matter and pure energy. While it assumes the shape of the physical body, it can travel to distant places while the physical body remains stationary. Furthermore, the shape of the astral body can be altered, resulting in the art of "shape shifting," as has been discussed. The astral body can, under certain conditions, be made to solidify while it is distant from the body, either in its human form or in a shape-shifted form. A thin connection must be maintained, though, between the physical body and the astral body or the person will die. This connection, the "silver cord," emanates from the Tan-tien.

Mythology

Western mystics make use of mythologies of the interactions of gods and goddesses to teach their students. Mythologies are not the ignorant ramblings of simple-minded people, but rather a highly sophisticated method of teaching emotional and mental balance and of living a life of harmony with nature and our fellow humans. It is the language of wisdom.

For example, to explain the change of seasons and the accompanying change in the length of daylight, the Greek myth of Demeter is used. Demeter was a goddess of the crops (specifically corn) and Persephone, her daughter, caused the sun to shine.

One day, Pluto, the god of the Underworld (the world of death and rebirth), captured Persephone to make her his wife. Demeter came down to earth in anger, causing crops to fail everywhere. People begged Demeter to come to some sort of compromise with Pluto so the people wouldn't starve. A compromise was finally reached in which Persephone was allowed to stay with her mother for half the year and with Pluto the other half. This is why half the year is sunny and warm and the other half is cold, with a weak sun.

Details of the myth vary depending on what deeper meanings the teller wishes to convey. Corn, for example, can represent the health of the body, and Demeter thus represents our physical well-being. The Underworld represents the meditative state, a time of dormancy and contemplation, which is the general mood of winter.

Our energies must be balanced between our practical, physical concerns and our spiritual needs. We are children of the physical world in the sense that all of us are concerned with this level of existence. But it often takes a personal calamity such as a nervous breakdown (Pluto capturing Persephone) to make us realize that there must be more to life. It then takes a personal commitment (her marriage to Pluto), such as to a meditative practice, to join with the inner being. To completely explore all levels of interpretation of even a single myth would take volumes.

Now let's take one particular Western myth and analyze it in a way which is perhaps startling but certainly refreshing. The Devil is portrayed as an angel who rebelled against God, as he wanted to become independent. God cast him out of heaven into hell beneath the earth. There evil souls are tormented for eternity by burning in fire. The Devil constantly tempts our souls to capture them and bring them into his dominion. A belief in God and an adherence to a godly way of life will keep us from succumbing to this horrible fate. Blind faith is required for a belief in God, as reason is not strong enough to lead you to the Supreme Being. Not even worship of an idol is allowed, for the Supreme Being is not a form which can be seen.

The T'ai-chi interpretation of this myth is this: the Devil is the thinking mind, which seeks independence from the instinctual, earth-connected BM, and from the primordial Tao. The mind was cast out of heaven (became separated from the BM). Thoughts of the mind tempt us, entrap our entire being with pre-set, programmed responses so that we cannot be truly free. (Heaven is the spontaneity of a life lived from BM.) Fire (representing thoughts and rational knowledge) constantly torments us. Only a belief in BM and reconnection to it can save us. BM cannot be reached through reason, only through faith, that is, by choosing to believe in this alternate world view.

We must let go of our rigid self-imagery and develop a fluid identity. We must not worship an idol—an image. The true self is structureless. The Tao which has a form is not the ultimate Tao. This is a perfect example of how a comparative study of mythology and several world views can shed more light on each and on the evolution of the human mind.

Nature Teachings

Allied with mythology is the use of the lessons of nature as a teaching device. The student is urged to live his life in accordance with the seasons. Spring is a time for planting seeds. This refers to new projects and relationships. Summer is a time for the growth of such projects, jsut as it is a time for the growth of plants. Earth's energy pattern at this time is conducive to growth of all kinds, including emotional growth and physical activity to promote the strengthening of the body.

During the fall, crops are harvested. This is a good time for reaping the fruits of your labors. A relationship may be consummated. A new business may start bringing in a profit. Winter is a time of contemplation and rest. Trees and plants are in a state of dormancy. Huddled around the fireplace (or kerosene heater), people tell stories of their summer adventures. A general feeling of coziness pervades the household. This is a time to consolidate the gains you have made previously.

"Look at the deer," a teacher might say. "During warmer weather, they fatten up on the lush vegetation. As the temperature drops, some begin to weaken. Perhaps they are very young or very old. Perhaps they did not fatten themselves enough. Some of those weakened deer will not make it through the winter. This may be the last year some of the old ones were destined to live anyway. It is time for them to move on to the next level of existence, having experienced all that a deer can experience in one lifetime. Others will die because they never got a real foothold on life. Still others, having put on enough weight during the summer, will regain their strength and make it through the winter.

"And so you students are like these deer. Some of you have gained a well-grounded and balanced knowledge of the teaching you are involved in. When self-doubt arises, when other activities tempt you to give up your studies, you remain steadfast. Others of you have not put your full effort into the teaching, and so every little distraction and doubt leads you away from it. Your determination weakens; you may actually leave the teaching. Still others have gained all they need from this teaching and now it is time to move on to other teachings.

"As winter approaches and your inner strength is tested, think of the lesson of the deer and determine which deer you are."

The Western Mystical World View

The pyramid is an excellent model of Western mysticism. At its base are four points and four sides, representing the four elements, Earth, Air, Fire and Water. Above is the fifth point, representing spirit. Whether pyramids were intentionally used as a model for that world view is open to debate. In my view, this elemental system was so central to the philosophy of ancient Egypt and to the American Indians, who also built pyramids, that it seems likely this was so.

The real self is the apex of the pyramid, spirit. This spirit must create "bodies" (or structures) to function in each of the four planes of existence, the physical body, the emotional body, the mental body and the body of will. There are other planes of existence as well, such as the astral planes, and bodies must also be fashioned to exist on those levels.

The mental plane, for example, is composed of thoughts and the energies which govern them. These thoughts are not limited by physical bodies. They move about the mental plane and may pass through people as radio waves pass through radio antennas. When a radio is tuned into that frequency, it emits the sounds which are being transmitted. Thoughts, emotions and even will can be transmitted in this way and picked up by others. You may believe it was your idea to do something, but that idea may actually have been planted in you by another person. I have to be careful when I'm around psychics. I often find myself getting up to make a pot of herbal tea when I know I don't want any. On the other hand, the psychic is very sensitive to other peoples' messages. Everyone has this sense, but may not be aware of it or have the words to express it. People in long-term relationships become tuned into each other in this manner.

The ability to know the difference between your own emotions, desires and thoughts and those of others is central to the work of psychic development. When you are independent of the maze of man-made influences around you, there will be no confusion in your life. You will be in control. On the other hand, there are people who purposefully send mental or emotional impulses to others to overcome their will. This is termed Black Magic, as opposed to White Magic, which is used for healing and other positive purposes.

In one interpretation of the Western mystical world view, each plane creates the plane below itself. Thus the mental plane creates the emotional and this, in turn, creates the physical. But I know of no serious practitioners of this system who go along with this idea. These practitioners would argue that the above interpretation really relates to the direction of the flow of energy through the planes.

Every practitioner has his own opinions and perspectives. When the teachers of a system or of several systems get together, they laugh over their differences as they guzzle down their wine. More likely, they gossip about those teachers who didn't come to the get-together, tell dirty jokes and do anything but speak of spiritual things.

There have been some instances, however, in which controversies were not taken in such a light-hearted manner. The Gnostics were wiped out by the early Catholics around 300 A.D. because the Gnostics believed that we are all in touch with God, while the Catholics believed that only the clergy were in touch with God. There were no Gnostic priests as such. Each person took turns being priest. Even pagans were allowed to join in. The Catholics, though, were interested in building a world religious empire and were not so liberal.

There is an understanding in the Western mystical system of the cyclic nature of time. The world goes through a cycle of twelve periods of about two thousand years each. We are about to enter a new phase of this cycle—the Age of Aquarius. Each age confers its qualities upon each of the planes, changing the nature of human interactions. The soul, however, evolves linearly. That is, each lifetime brings it new wisdom and experience, and once it has gained enough of both, it passes on to the next level of existence, and so on. The power it has gained in its cyclic adventures propels it forward into the next realm, just as a rock tied to a string may be spun around several times and then released, traveling in a straight line to a target. The soul's target is said to be union with the Supreme Being. This Being has sent Its consciousness down into the world by structuring Its originally unstructured consciousness. The structured "bodies" It has created in order to experience life then return to their Source to enrich It. This world view explains that when you realize that this is the purpose of life, and that the soul itself is immortal, the fears and petty concerns of life fade away.

Comparison of Western and Eastern Teachings

With this discussion of the Western mystical system, we can see how different cultures approach the task of teaching similar principles and skills. We can see more clearly the uniqueness of T'ai-chi and place it within a wider context of teachings dealing with human development. By understanding which aspects of a teaching are cultural and which are universal, we can pick out those universal aspects without necessarily having to adopt a foreign culture. In addition, we can gain an appreciation for the creativity involved in developing techniques for leading students to higher states of consciousness.

You may have already noticed many similarities between Western mysticism and T'ai-chi-Ch'uan, as well as many differences. If our task is to create a world free from the threat of ecological destruction, war, repression of the human spirit and intolerance, then we may have to create a new culture, borrowing from the best parts of those already existing. A comparative study of the fundamental building blocks of each culture is essential to such a quest.

In my discussions with advanced teachers of Western mysticism, I have often heard that in its deeper teachings, this system is actually more similar to T'ai-chi-Ch'uan than one would suppose. It is only at the level of student, these people say, that differences seem to exist. My argument is that very few people ever reach those advanced stages of any teaching. For those people, the stage of advanced student is about as far as they will ever reach. Most do not even go that far, being part of a popular culture which is a watered-down version of the deeper teachings of that culture. As teachers, we must deal with what is actually meaningful to people's everyday lives. That is why I have tried to bring the teaching of T'ai-chi-Ch'uan, as well as Western mysticism, down to everyday terms.

How many people in our Western society study the Qabala? Yet that ancient system lies at the heart of our culture. A Qabala master might argue that our popular culture has strayed so far from its origins that it has little to do with the Qabala. Yet, I feel that by studying the origins of each culture, we can gain great insights as to how the popular version of that culture evolved. In so doing, we can understand our own lives much more clearly, even though we may not be students of the deeper and more mysterious teachings.

Western mysticism is not really a unified system, as is T'ai-chi-Ch'uan. It borrows a little from many cultures: Egyptian, Celtic, Druidic, Sumerian, Babylonian, Hebraic, etc. Therefore, each teacher and school of teaching is slightly different. In the above description of Western mysticism, I have tried to stay within the bounds of general agreement, in order to give a more unified picture of what might otherwise appear to be an incomprehensible system. My apologies to those who are actually involved in this system for not giving a more complete account of it. My purpose is not to write a book about Western mysticism, but to use it as a contrast to the real subject of this book, T'ai-chi-Ch'uan. With the above in mind, let's examine the similarities and differences between these two major world teachings.

Comparison of Philosophies

All systems of knowledge and personal development assume that there is some underlying pattern to the universe and that a union with or awareness of that pattern will lead to improvements in one's life. In Western mysticism, the emphasis is on a conscious, mental knowledge of that pattern. (In Chinese philosophy, the equivalent would be the Confucian school). This pattern is taught in terms of a mathematical model. Mathematics plays such a vital role that the Bible is said to be written in mathematical language.

Taoism also uses a mathematical system consisting of the eight trigrams and sixty-four hexagrams of the *I Ching*, the Book of Changes. But the emphasis in this Eastern system is on direct experience of those natural forces. A student will not sit for hours reading books, but will spend time in the forest. If he has questions about spiritual matters, he will ask the trees, squirrels and water spirits.

T'ai-chi-Ch'uan is feeling- and body-oriented, while Western mysticism is mind- and thought- oriented. Unfortunately, many in the latter discipline neglect their physical well-being and seek their advancement only in the mind. There is a belief prevalent in Western disciplines that thoughts are "higher" or somehow more spiritual than the body. I discussed before how stomach cells might think of you, their God, as a great stomach. Many in Western circles consider God to be a vast thinking mind. Advanced teachers may say that God is indeed mind, but by mind they mean "that primordial emptiness, the power of creativity (Tao), and not thinking per se," and that the body is as important as thinking.

But most students I have encountered miss this subtlety. In fact, our entire culture is not very health-oriented. A common interpretation of Western philosophy is that the farther you get away from the physical earth the more spiritual you are. Anything natural is to be avoided.

In the West, that single, thinking Entity controls the universe. The T'ai-chi version of our universe is more ecological. At each level, there is a balancing system, a BM. This BM does not operate by thinking; it does not rain down terror on those who do not worship it, as in Western religions. It is simply a balancing process. When an imbalance is created, the entire system rebalances itself. It is by living in balance that we can maintain our well-being. Fear of God will not help.

The Qabala is actually a scheme of balance as well. The central pillar represents the middle path between the two extremes. The Sephiroth representing the God-consciousness sits at the top of the middle pillar. This Sephiroth, Kether, is part of you as it is part of everyone. Actually it would be more accurate to say that everyone is part of Kether, for at this level, individuality has not been created yet.

Here is an example of the difference between the popular culture and the deeper teachings of that culture: God has become anthropomorphized for popular consumption. God as we know Him from Sunday school is more profitable than God as a balancing system.

On one point, both systems agree. Our true reality is pure creativity. The God of the West created the earth and everything on it. In T'ai-chi-Ch'uan we identify with pure creativity and experience our entire world—our bodies as well as the trees—as produced equally by this creativity.

But beyond this point there is a divergence. In many Western mystical schools, the emphasis is on using the mind to gain independence from this creativity, this cosmic balancing system. Fire represents knowledge, as opposed to pure creativity, which is based on the principle of balance. The tendency of the mind to move to extremes is balanced by the tendency of BM to remain centered. Our possible demise through nuclear annihilation makes Fire even more potent as a symbol. The thinking mind is seen as a tool to control nature and impose our will (also represented by Fire) upon it.

T'ai-chi-Ch'uan is quite different. The emphasis is on merging with the flow of nature. The story is told of a T'ai-chi master walking with his pupil. The pupil saw an old man dive into the rapids of a river. After a couple of minutes, the pupil prepared to dive in after the old man to save his life.

"Wait!" insisted his teacher. When the old man finally came up, the teacher spoke to his pupil.

"You see? He is unharmed. That man is a T'ai-chi master. Where the water pulls him in, he goes in. Where it throws him out, he comes out. He flows with the currents and is thereby safe."

When the individual awareness unites with the planetary awareness, the will of the planetary BM is allowed to flow through the individual and he becomes a messenger of nature, a messenger of harmony.

The mind is seen in the West as being perfected to reach the Supreme Being. But from an Eastern perspective, the mind can never truly reach that level of awareness; it can only grab for it. T'ai-chi-Ch'uan develops spontaneity in the individual, the ability to be straightforward and drop self-consciousness while retaining true self-awareness. In this way, you slip into the state of harmony and do not have to grab for it. T'ai-chi-Ch'uan is really a process of letting go of mind, rather than making it even more powerful than it already is. By giving up the illusion of separation, your consciousness unites with your subconscious, your dreaming state with your waking state, your mind with your body and your BM with the BM of other beings (human and nonhuman).

Another form which the Western orientation of separation takes is that of the planes of existence. There are said to be many such planes or levels, of which the astral planes are examples. We develop a separate "body" for each plane. T'ai-chi-Ch'uan emphasizes the basic energy pattern from which all forms of awareness arise. Awareness of this central energy pattern is the focus of the teaching. The various "levels of existence" are not seen as separate regions, but as all one place. And that place is the one we are in now. Each "plane" is merely another viewing angle of the same thing as seen by different inner senses (the energy senses).

The Western teachings particularize these viewing angles as if they were different locations. This is due to the matter-oriented viewpoint of the West (that of the world as separate objects bouncing into each other). This has an enormous impact on our lives. If heaven, for example, is seen as "another place," then we will be less concerned with what happens to "this place." The Western-world-view people may shoot off in a cosmic rocket ship to heaven, but what about us poor Taoists who have to stay here and live in this polluted mess?

T'ai-chi-Ch'uan is process-oriented (energy-oriented) rather than matter-oriented. It sees things as processes of balance and interdependence. "Heaven" is not separate from the physical planet, but is seen as a more harmonious state of being. Yet, Western mysticism recognizes energy as well. In both systems there are exercises to send a flow of energy up the chakras. In my dealings with Western teachers, I find agreement on the importance of sending energy up the chakras, but not as much agreement on sending it back down into the earth.

T'ai-chi emphasizes that what you take from the earth you must return, and this includes energy. There must be a circular flow, yin and yang, so that the energy which is raised may be grounded as well. Some Western practitioners will raise the energy and then, when their work (healing, for example) is done, they will ground themselves. T'ai-chi-Ch'uan practices grounding energy at the same time as raising it.

There is an interesting similarity in the East and West in regard to energy. Both world views believe that physical creatures are not the only ones who inhabit this world. There are many energy beings around us, who, because of the undeveloped senses of most people, cannot be seen by them. Those living in Taoist temples are very respectful of energy beings, lest these beings cause trouble for them. Western magicians evoke the beings and learn to visualize them in order to use them for various purposes.

The power animals of the shamans have often been thought of as these energy beings. I feel they are best categorized as energy patterns because a power animal is supposed to be part of a person from birth as a "protector." Thus they seem to be a natural part of the person himself. That person can then acquire more power animals which will also stay with him. The energy beings of East and West do not have these qualities.

Saying that energy beings are a product of the student's imagination is meaningless because the student himself is a product of the imagination of the original creative energy. He is therefore on the same level as these energy beings and must deal with them carefully, as one would deal with an animal encountered in the wild. Being made of energy, they have the ability to affect our energy patterns for good or evil. The more the student can merge with the creative force, the stronger is his position with the energy beings. The T'ai-chi student uses Chi-Gung and (internal) Push Hands in his dealings with energy beings, while the Western mystic uses magical ritual.

Comparison of Teaching Methods

In both systems you find the elements. Taoism has its Wood, Fire, Earth, Metal and Water corresponding to east, south, center, west and north, and to spring, summer, long summer, fall and winter. In both, nature is used as a teaching device. But in this regard, Western mysticism may be divided into two components: one is magical and oriented to gaining power over nature; the other is religious and emphasizes worship of nature. The lesson of the deer falls into this category. But here again, this is often more mental in practice than actual. I have found very few in Western mysticism who are into camping in the woods (unless there are a bathroom, showers and a fast-food place nearby), while I have found few in T'ai-chi-Ch'uan who aren't.

Both systems are hermetic. This means that deeper truths are hidden in parables, myths and such devices as the elements. The student progresses to deeper and deeper levels of meaning. While the raw material in the West is mental (myths), in T'ai-chi-Ch'uan it is mostly movement. A quality of the Form will be used to illustrate a deeper truth.

There is an exception to this mental orientation of Western mysticism. A study of the teachings of Jesus (especially those expurged from the Bible, such as the Book of Thomas) reveal a more physical orientation. Jesus was the physical embodiment of God, according to Church teachings. In one of the sayings allowed to remain in the Bible, Jesus tells his people that they can enter heaven only through him, that is, through the physical plane. But then Jesus is reported to have traveled through India and Tibet during his adolescence and early adulthood, studying and lecturing. The people of these areas still refer to "Saint Issa" with reverence, and there are supposedly records of his travels which several people claim to have seen and translated.

A particular individual may have a different slant on his teaching than his own teachers. What are we to say about such individuals? Are they heretics or are they creative and independent? In the end, each person must sort things out for himself. Blind obedience to any teacher is foolish.

There is the story of a Zen teacher who periodically sent his head student off to the woods for a six-month communion with nature. The teacher, abbot of a monastery, would tell his student each time that he was not yet ready to teach.

One day, the student returned from one of his communions. His air was confident and he strode over to the abbot. His teacher, noticing the student's hautiness, slapped him in the face, whereupon the student slapped his teacher back. The abbot went back to his room, packed his things and left the monastery, giving charge of it to his head student.

The meditation in the woods of Zen or T'ai-chi is quite different from the meditation of a Qabalist. The latter will think about each of the Sephiroth of the Tree of Life. There is the tendency in the West, to meditate *about* something, to think about it. T'ai-chi meditation consists of letting go of thought. Concerntration without thinking is the basis of Eastern meditation. It is said that when one lets in even a single thought, the entire universe comes along with it. The mind must be emptied of thought and then the power of concentration is immense. It is like a focused laser beam. This power is used for healing, traveling the realm of consciousness states, developing the energy senses and strengthening BM and its connection to the earth.

When the meditation student first experiences the power emanating from the chakras, he is quite startled. He has a tiger by the tail. In the West, the student learns to use this energy by healing or by "asking" or praying for favors from the god or power of his belief. In T'ai-chi-Ch'uan, we also use it for healing, but naturally, we develop the power through the use of the Form, Push Hands and

Kung-Fu. The chakra Forms, in which we use the focused power to propel us through the Form, is one example. In this manner, we practice centering our attention in each chakra. This means that instead of our minds controlling our actions or even our BMs, we now experiment with each of the chakras controlling our movements. We "sink into" each chakra, giving up our mind-centered identity. We see "through the eyes" of each of the chakras.

This is certainly a difficult thing to comprehend. But when it happens to a student, the student has no doubt that it has happened. When that student recalls the words describing such a phenomenon, whether in this book or others, he will say, "Yes! This must be what he was talking about in that book." That is one of the uses of this book. When you experience something that has been mentioned, look it up and read what else is said about that feeling. Determine whether my experiences match yours. Use this book as a road map of consciousness.

Naturally, I prefer the T'ai-chi approach to chakra work over the Western approach. Forgive me if my bias shows, but my past seven years of study of Western mysticism should be enough to prove my great respect and admiration for the Western system as well. In my opinion, the Western approach does not emphasize the ability to be free from your own mind and fully sink into the power of BM. You cannot ride the waves of energy like a surfer, sailing through the air on the crest of a wave. You must stay on the shore, appreciating the wave's beauty, sending it prayers of appeal and gratitude. This of course does not hold true for those who have penetrated the outer teachings, but those are few.

As this book is really designed for the general reader, I will resist the temptation to delve into this subject in greater depth, reserving my many opinions on the subject for late-night bull sessions with those who are there to defend their systems from the onslaught of an irreverent writer. Nor do I wish to be rapped on the knuckles by my own Western teachers.

Both systems attempt to raise each individual to the highest level of human skill, while at the same time retaining an attitude of simplicity which creates harmonious interpersonal relations. The magical aspect of each is the development of skill, while a closeness to nature develops simplicity in one's life.

Sacrifice

The attitude of simplicity is best exemplified in each system through the teaching technique of sacrifice. In the West it is called "libation." A small quantity of wine is spilled from your cup to give something to the gods, as the gods give to humans. A small part of the cake you eat during a ceremony is likewise libated. Jokes are made about going to the bathroom to "libate to the gods," but it's really not a joke. Our lives consist of giving as well as taking. An equal measure of both results in a balanced life. And when our time comes to shed our bodies, we are actually libating our bodies, returning them to the gods.

In T'ai-chi-Ch'uan, we may even go too far in our libations. We not only let go of our tension and fear, we let go of our minds as well. Rather than saying we lose our minds, I would rather say we *loose* our minds. Giving up mental conflicts results in a loose body. There are a lot of T'ai-chi teachers running around loose.

Giving up addictive dependence on the mind and programming results in a freer, more fulfilling, healthier life. The trick is to know *what* to give up. Give your tension and fear to the gods. There is a song which goes

If somehow you could pack up all your sorrows
And give them all to me,
You would lose them;
I know how to use them,
Give them all to me.

You want to get rid of your sorrows. The greater forces in this world ask you to give your sorrows to them. For sorrows, like everything else in this world, are nothing but energy. If you don't want them, give them back to the earth.

Sometimes we get into the habit of grabbing for more. If we could learn to give as skillfully as we learn to take, our lives would be much richer. Both East and West agree on this. Yet there are those students who even try to grab for enlightenment. They feel incomplete or inferior in some way and believe that "achieving enlightenment" is the answer to their problems.

Enlightenment

What is this elusive quality or state of being for which millions of people have striven throughout history? This state of enlightenment seems to be the purpose, the central issue of many of the world's religions and philosophical systems. Is this state of perfection real or is it just a product of the imagination of a few gurus? I'll begin by relating two stories—one told by Gautama Buddha and one which I experienced several years ago:

Gautama said that enlightenment can be imagined as a father returning home to see his house engulfed in flames. He calls to his children, "Come out! I have brought each of you the gift you most want." The children run out of the house and are saved. But they are disappointed to find the father has not really brought them any gifts.

The second story involves my visit to a lecture given by the student of some Indian guru (I forget who). He spoke of how wonderful enlightenment was and went into throes of ecstasy whenever he even mentioned the word.

I felt obliged to ask the obvious question: "Are you, yourself, enlightened?"

"No," he replied.

"If you're not enlightened, how do you know what it's like?"

"Well, I can just imagine it!"

Perhaps you have had times in your life when you have experienced beautiful feelings. It may have been a summer day, watching the sunset. You were in good health, with no cares, enjoying another's company or your own, and you felt wonderful. But next day, the everyday problems of life faced you once again and your peaceful feeling was disrupted. If only we could feel every day the way we felt that one summer evening! Perhaps this is what the student of the Indian guru was imagining.

To many, enlightenment means a lifetime of remaining in a particular state. Enlightenment is thus a form of pleasant rigidity. The problem with this version of enlightenment is that we are living creatures and not stones. It is appropriate for a stone to remain in a stationary state for a long time, but inappropriate for a human.

A living creature is sensitive to its environment. Its internal state changes from moment to moment to adjust to its changing environment. It fails to respond to its environment only when it is dead. In a state of sensitivity, the animal is connected to its environment. The teaching of connection and harmony between the individual and the environment is the basis of T'ai-chi-Ch'uan. Harmonizing with the environment does not mean being a slave to it or completely giving up your will. By being aware of the forces acting upon you and learning to work with and not against them, your life becomes easier and more effective. Only a minimum interference with the environment is needed to create desired changes.

I have heard people describing meditation as a way to block out the world and become numb. To them, this state of numbness is enlightenment. In T'ai-chi-Ch'uan we develop our naturalness, our creaturehood, spontaneity, sensitivity and awareness. I do not believe that Western metaphysics necessarily requires a separation from the environment, but that is the way it has been popularly interpreted. Development in the West has been characterized by this separation, which is seen as an independence and growth of the human race. Certainly we have achieved much from this line of development. Modern technology and medicine attest to the powers of an independent mind. On a psychic level, the development of a pattern of energy within the individual, independent of external forces, allows the individual to repel negative energies directed against him by others.

But this independence has been accomplished only with great sacrifice. The sacrifice we have made is, in my view, an improper one. Through the science of ecology, we are beginning to become aware of the effects of our technology on the physical environment. Within us, the separation of mind from body has had disastrous health effects. Emotionally, the ability to feel close to and share with others has suffered.

To a person suffering hypersensitivity to others, the blockage of external energies which results from mind-body separation may serve as a convenient quick fix. For a society of people needing protection from disease and famine, the development of environmentally damaging modern technologies may have been a necessary stage of development. But neither are long-term solutions. The search for enlightenment may, for its part, be a necessary stage in the spiritual development of an individual. It may serve to start him on the road to personal growth.

Harmonizing the Extremes

In each case, harmony or integration is the long-term solution, harmony of the individual with the environment, mind with body, technology with natural lifestyles, striving for a goal with the joy of life as it is, and social independence with emotional sharing. On a larger level, a harmonizing of the Eastern approach with the Western approach is taking place.

Many years ago, Indian Buddhism was brought to China, where it met the prevailing culture, Taoism. Several generations of students later, the two melded into "Ch'an" or "Zen," a Buddhist form of Taoism. Just as the high metaphysics of India blended with the down-to-earth simplicity of China, a similar occurrence is taking place today in this country. T'ai-chi, Zen and American Indian tradition are blending with the high metaphysics of the West and with science. The progeny of this mating promises to be as unique as the Ch'an of China. For its part, Western culture has spread to the East, and there may be a corresponding amalgamation of those cultures as well.

At the Long Island School of T'ai-chi-Ch'uan, I emphasize the balance of mind and body, consciousness and subconscious. But since the students have grown up in a culture which emphasizes only one side of the human potential, I concentrate on the other—subconscious, instinctive body awareness. The balance which I try to develop in the student leads to naturalness, calm, spontaneity, joy, health and sensitivity.

One of the stages the student must go through is the discovery of the many tricks the mind has been playing on him to keep him unhappy. These tricks are in the nature of dividing the world into pairs of opposites. The person whose behavior is controlled by this dualistic activity of mind then searches for truth as opposed to falsehood, good as opposed to evil, masculine as opposed to feminine behavior, enlightenment as opposed to an ordinary state of being. Rather than leading to balance, these searches lead to living at one or the other extreme of the dualistic pairs.

Part of the Zen teaching is to give the student a Koan or question to answer. A famous Koan asks, "What is the sound of one hand clapping?" The student may spend many weeks or years pondering this question before he realizes that his very pondering, the activity of the mind, is the sound of one hand clapping. The mind searches for only one half of the world—the half which is correct, true, real. It thus corners the entire organism in a small cage made of its own particular system of ideas and concepts, one of which is the idea of enlightenment. Enlightenment is the illusory gift of the Buddha to save you from your burning life. It helps to spur you on toward personal growth. But if you remain unhappy at not having achieved enlightenment, then you are missing the point.

If you did not hold an idea of perfection and imperfection in your mind, then you wouldn't seek perfection in the first place. The mind tells you that you're not what you're supposed to be. You must become enlightened or perfected to be acceptable and respected or "spiritual." A political leader does much the same.

He tells us we must fight some other country to be secure. Politics are the mind of the macrocosm. While many people are wise to the tricks of the macrocosmic mind, they are not so wise to the mind of the microcosm.

Zen and T'ai-chi have often been likened to a raft which helps you get from one side of a river to the other. When you reach the other side, you must abandon the raft. It is no longer needed. This process of letting go is essential in personal growth. Otherwise you may spend your life adrift on a spiritual raft. Zen students who have made just such a mistake are said to "stink of Zen." They become very self-centered, believing that the point of life is to force yourself into some rigid state of experience. They miss out on sharing their lives with others, which is so essential to fulfillment. And then, when they finally achieve this rigid state, they are not enlightened, but deadened, and are not happy anyway. They are involved in a loser's game and miss out on life itself.

Some get involved in the search for enlightenment because they believe they will be able to perform great feats of magic. There is another Zen story of a student of Hinduism and a student of Zen. The Hindu student said, "Come see my teacher. He performs great feats of magic. He can stand on one side of a river and tell you what someone has written on a paper on the other side of the river. He can remain buried underground for a month and come out alive."

The Zen student was not impressed. "My teacher can perform even greater feats of magic. When he is tired, he sleeps. When hungry, he eats."

The point is that we don't realize how magical our everyday life is. Think of the magic of the seasons, of birth, of love, the magic of sitting around a campfire at night listening to hoot owls. The acorn grows into the mighty oak with no spiritual training. Our earth never went to a temple, yet it spins around its axis and around the sun unerringly. Compared to that, what are the feats of the guru? Sometimes we feel that only those things which are unnatural are to be praised.

Zen has been called the teaching of hauling water, chopping wood, to show that its theme is developing harmony with the environment by living a natural life.

Yet some people associate enlightenment with living unnaturally. I have heard many stories of gurus who were admired because they did not eat or drink (even water), had no sex and did not even move, but sat for years in one position. This was considered to be the height of spiritual development. Their idea is to overcome their natural desires with their will. In this way they are living at the extreme and have left the middle path. Their minds are still in control, grabbing for the extreme. The essential principle of balance has been neglected. The mind is needed, for it helps us reach outward to explore. But BM is needed as well, for it keeps us connected to the center of balance and does not allow us to stray too far. To overcome one part of us with another shows that there are still battles within us.

American Indian Culture

The comparative study of world cultures is a method of balancing. By borrowing a little from each culture and blending these ingredients with our own creativity, we can develop a balanced way of life, free from the rigidities of any one culture.

Another nature-oriented group of cultures is that of the American Indian. While there are numerous Indian nations, cultures and languages, a common element among all of them is living in harmony with nature. (Of course, many Indians now live in inner cities or impoverished reservations, but there is a strong upsurge back to traditional lifestyles.)

The "vision quest" is a central component of Indian culture. A "vision" refers to the vision of your life, why you are in this world. In a typical vision quest, the young man (and woman, nowadays) will fast and meditate for several days before the actual vision quest. Ritual cleansing is done each day. The aspirant then leaves for a prearranged spot in nature, perhaps a cave or a clearing in the woods. He carries only his clothes, perhaps some water and his sacred objects. The quest lasts from one to four days and hopefully culminates in a vision. This may take the form of the sight of some being talking to the quester, a dream or even a realization or reaffirmation of a previous understanding.

His activities during this time are limited to praying, using the sacred objects in ceremony, perhaps stretching a few times a day, visiting the latrine, sleeping and mostly meditating. The vision is sacred and the respect he gains from the community has a great deal to do with the vision and how it is carried out.

My own vision was given to me by my father, who identified closely with nature. Almost from the time I was born, I was encouraged to crawl around in the forest and among the chickens and vegetables of the farm next door. At the same time, I was instructed in Hebrew philosophy by my parents and in eliminating cultural conditioning. While my vision was handed down to me, I fully accept it and of course have tailored it to suit my own taste.

One form of ritual purification common among many Indian nations is the "sweat lodge." Imagine a hut about twelve feet long, eight feet wide and four feet high. It is covered with canvas and plastic (hides in the old days). Inside, a large pit has been dug in the earth. From ten to twenty people crowd into the hut, sitting around the perimeter, facing inward. A large fire outside heats twenty or so large rocks red hot.

Inside, the "sweat leader" and the people chant. The sacred pipe is passed around. The sweat leader calls to the fire-tender to bring seven rocks. These are dropped into the pit, one by one, and each is welcomed as it enters. It is night. Within the hut, only the red glow of the rocks is visible. The scent of herbs, which litter the floor, mingles with the smell of the burning rocks. More chanting and admonitions by the sweat leader to live a more natural, harmonious life. A gourd of water is thrown onto the rocks, sending gushes of steam into already hot faces.

More water, more steam, and quarts of sweat seem to pour off each body. Another group of rocks is brought into the sweat lodge and the entire process is repeated. Four sessions in all represent the four elements.

The bowl of the pipe represents Earth, while the burning mixture and the burning rocks represent Fire. Water is represented by the water in the gourd and Air by the sweet smell of herbs. The sweat lodge itself represents the pipe bowl (in which prayers are symbolically "smoked") and the womb. While interpretations differ as to what represents what, and the sweat of each nation is different, the ceremony cleanses body and soul, the body through sweating and the soul through the symbolic ritual. The "moon time" of women is said to be their form of cleansing. While the men have only the sweat lodge, the women have the sweat plus menstruation.

In my first sweat experience, there were twenty people packed very tightly, so that all but the most minor movements were impossible. The door flap was shut. I made a quick calculation of the amount of oxygen in the hut and the number of people consuming it and came to a pessimistic conclusion. Body heat made the hut unbearable. When the first rocks were brought in, our sweat leader told us that we would see our spirits. I began looking for a spirit, but the heat was so intense, the cramped quarters so uncomfortable and the oxygen so thin, I began to panic. Then I realized that I had indeed seen my spirit, for I had seen my own fear. Since one of the conditions of our participating was that no one would leave, all I could do was to trust in my own power to survive and to my connection to the earth, as well as trusting my sweat brothers and sisters. Leaving would be impossible anyway, as the only path out lay across the red-hot rocks. I made a prayer to the earth, asking her to give me strength and calm and immediately relaxed.

Our sweat leader suggested that we place our hands on the earth to make prayers to her. I noticed that the earth was cool. My hands never left the earth for the rest of the sweat. I thought what a good technique this was for demonstrating our dependence on the earth. In fact, our sweat leader's main message was to protect the earth, for she has given so much to us and we have treated her so poorly.

In the little hut, all participants had to work together. As the pipe was handed around, each person helped the one next to him fumble for the pipe. Our leader emphasized that we had to help and support each other. This built a feeling of community and mutual support. The insistence that we not leave the hut was symbolically important as well. As hot and uncomfortable as the sweat lodge got, we had to work together to survive. The same is true of our planet as a whole. We cannot leave the earth, so as polluted and crowded as our planet gets, we must work together to survive. There is no escape. Belief in the coming earth renewal, a period of great geologic upheaval beginning around the latter part of this decade, is common in American Indian legends. Thus the belief in strong communities trained for wilderness survival is also common.

After our four rounds, we left the sweat lodge and several participants collapsed. The sweat next to us was apparently more intense. We had heard much crying and screaming, and when their sweat ended, they barely crawled out.

The vision quest and the sweat lodge are but two of the rich and varied traditions of the American Indian nations. They give us the flavor of a strong nature-oriented culture.

Science

There is one more "culture" to be discussed and that is science. I include science as a culture because it has its own precepts, its own perspectives and its own impact on the lifestyle of the citizens of a science-oriented society. The way of life of a city living in the midst of the scientific revolution is quite different from that of a jungle village only recently discovered by outsiders. It is different not only in the obvious technological advances, but in the way those advances affect the culture.

Scientific societies (that is, organizations of scientists in specific fields) began stretching their muscles around the 1500s in Europe, becoming independent of the political power of the Church. The Catholic Church, resigning itself to the growing power of and respect for scientists in the eyes of the public, could at least find solace in the scientists' hands-off policy in regards to spiritual matters. Science would concern itself with the material world alone and would leave spiritual studies to the Church. Science thus became a method of describing physical phenomena and discovering the causal connections between those phenomena.

Because of the power of the Church, subjects appropriate for scientific investigations had to be limited, avoiding any which might cause severe political repercussions. Although many scientists were, in fact, members or leaders of mystical orders, such beliefs or perspectives were respectfully hidden so as not to create problems for their scientific organizations.

Such limitations structured science in specific ways. Today, when science is respected as much as organized religion and no longer needs to bow down to the power of the Church, it could presumably blossom into a wider perspective. But as with all movements or traditions, once a structure has been set, it is hard to alter.

This structure has as its foundation the basic separation of the observer from the observed, the mind from the physical world and the individual from his surroundings. The connection between an individual and the environment, the heart of magical teachings, is strictly avoided except in the case of the science of ecology, which I consider to be a relatively new science. Certainly it is as new if not newer than quantum and relativity physics, also touted to have broken the limitations of traditional science.

These "new" sciences are now beginning to be felt on a cultural level. Interest in ecology and in the uniting of the scientific and spiritual realms has spurred interest in T'ai-chi, American Indian tradition and other alternate paths. But the feeling of separation and isolation, caused by the perspective of the world as isolated dead objects ruled by mathematical law, still persists in our culture. The idea of personal growth, vision quests and meditation is only beginning to leave the realm of ridicule in the minds of most people.

There is still a belief among many of us that science will yet solve all our problems and that meditation and spiritual studies are leftovers from an ignorant and barbaric past. The possible destruction of all life on earth, though, has given some people second thoughts. Perhaps there is more to life than mathematics, profits and more consumer goods. Science itself is merely a method of investigation. There is nothing inherent in its methods which limits it to its present perspectives. Such limitations are political, and I believe they will gradually dissolve.

From my viewpoint, there are two basic models or perspectives of science, which are now changing. One is the linear causal perspective. In this way of thinking, one thing causes another to happen. Then, that occurrence causes a third thing to happen, and so on in a linear way. This is the manner in which the universe operates. This perspective is obviously a reflection of our method of thinking. When thinking logically, one thought does indeed follow another. The world, then, is seen as a product of thought. This is a natural result of the Western mystical basis of Western culture.

The other perspective is that of the model of the solar system—a single powerful central entity surrounded by lesser beings drawn to its power. The old atomic model with its central nucleus and surrounding atoms derives from this model.

Let's take a look at another model, based on the nervous system. While the brain is the largest single collection of nerve synapses (exchanges of signals between nerves), there are several other such "ganglia" in the body. The solar plexus is a large collection of such nerve exchanges. Much of the nerve signals of the body never reach the brain, but are channeled through the solar plexus. The nervous system is, therefore, a more decentralized model in terms of power. In addition, the nervous system is an integrated system. That is, each activity of the individual nerves is affecting all the other nerves constantly. The muscles, endocrine and other activities of the body affected by the nervous system affect, in turn, the nerves. It would be impossible to separate out a linear sequence of nerve activities which could account for the entire functioning of the nervous system.

The centralized model of our universe has led to, or is an indication of, the centralization of attention of our nervous system through concentration on thinking. This, in turn, has led to many changes in our bodies and our health, as discussed previously. Development of a more decentralized, balanced/counterbalanced ecological model, such as the model of the decentralized nervous system, will have beneficial health effects on individuals. It may have political effects as well.

The linear perspective of causality, in which the universe is viewed as a one-line progression of events, has its base in the Western religious view of the Biblical predictions of the coming of a savior and the destruction of the earth in an apocalypse. Certainly the continuance of a nonecological way of life will ensure that the latter perspective will come true. Is it just a coincidence that the Western religious world view, with its belief in ultimate destruction, has finally developed a method to achieve it?

But we have the power to create a different future by creating a different model of life. The ecological perspective is harmonious with nature-oriented cultures, as they are cyclic in perspective rather than linear. Time, to them, proceeds in endless cycles of day and night and seasons, rather than in a single direction ending in oblivion. Even the earth renewal mentioned before is not a time of total destruction, but a cyclic phenonemon, such as the ice ages or earthquakes.

The study of cultural perspectives can give us great insight into the causes of our most urgent problems. As magicians, we can change our world by changing our perspectives. T'ai-chi provides a practical, down-to-earth perspective in keeping with both the science of ecology and theoretical physics. It is no wonder that the past few years have seen an incredible upsurge in interest in this ancient perspective. Its emphasis on the interdependence of all life, the untiy of the individual with his environment, of mind with body and of conscious with subconscious, provides a viable framework for the survival of life on this planet.

The Next Step

The Tasadays, that stone-age tribe in the Philippine jungles, stood at the edge of the clearing. They had never seen a clearing before and were frightened. All of a sudden a tiny bee appeared in the sky. As it came closer, it grew larger and louder until it turned into a giant bird. Its huge wing beat wind down upon them so that they could barely stand. Several tried to run away but were frozen in their tracks from fear. This was the end. The giant bird would swoop down upon them and eat the Tasadays to the last person.

But it was not their end. The helicopter delivering a team of scientists was a doorway into a new world, a world filled with new opportunities and new dangers. The innocence of the Tasaday was irrevocably shattered.

We, as a planetary culture, have also lost our innocence. We are faced with annihilation, not from a bee or a bird, but from our own ingenuity. We fear for our future. As the Tasaday were given new tools with which to improve their lives (at least technologically), we too have been given new tools. But these tools are not new to those cultures who are providing them to us. T'ai-chi, yoga, American Indian traditions, Western mysticism, etc., are the tools now surfacing which can prevent the end of the evolution of life on this planet. There are many such tools, all based on harmony with the environment. They are freely given and occur in such variety as to satisfy all our needs and temperaments.

There are cycles of perspectives as there are cycles of seasons. For a more savage, younger world, the development of a perspective nurturing technology may have been appropriate. But now the cycle has swung too far that way; nature-oriented perspectives are now more appropriate to our present problems.

Hopefully, we will find a balance in the middle.

As children, we needed to obtain tools to become powerful adults, so that we might provide for our needs. As adults, we need to learn to live harmoniously with our fellows by gaining inner power and wisdom. Our civilization may be considered adult now. It has certainly achieved external power. Now it needs to learn inner power, leading to harmony and peace.

A civilization grows, just as its individuals grow. The birth and growth of civilizations is an age-old process. Each thinks it has progressed further than any before. In my adolescence, when I first began studying oriental religions and Western mysticism and learning about the Qabala, I thought I had discovered knowledge my parents knew nothing about. Then, glancing through my grade-school yearbook, I found an entry by my father. It was a Taoist saying about emptiness. After my father's death, I told my mother about the Qabala. She showed me some of my father's books, among them books on the Qabala.

In our scientific world, we feel we have reached the height of achievement. Perhaps this is true technologically, but what are we as human beings? I have often felt that in our society, just remaining a decent, kind, aware human being is a great accomplishment. It shouldn't have to be so.

Do you have a vision of what this world should be like? Have you dreamed of a world safe from the threat of destruction? The earth renewal predicted by some cultures does not have to be geologic in nature. On one point there is agreement. If we empower ourselves, if we empower our dreams and renew our world internally, the earth will not have to renew itself in a physical sense. On a more down-to-earth level, a change to a more nature-oriented culture will solve many of the problems which sour our individual lives.

The power to change the culture is in your hands. Do not be fooled into thinking that you are powerless. If your vision can change your own life, the same vision of millions of people can change the world. You have the potential to become a powerful Taoist magician, and the first duty of a magician is to heal. By healing your own life, you will help to heal the entire planet.